The Hopeless Hen

AND OTHER ANIMAL TAILS

GRACE FOX ANDERSON, first editor of Winner Books, is editor of *Counselor,* and *Primary Days,* Scripture Press' take-home papers for children 6 to 11. She has been in church-related ministries with children for over 25 years. Mrs. Anderson received her degree in Christian Education from Wheaton College in Wheaton, Ill. Her stories and articles have been published in a variety of Christian magazines. She has also compiled the stories in the popular Winner Books' Animal Tails series: *The Hairy Brown Angel and Other Animal Tails, The Peanut Butter Hamster and Other Animal Tails, Skunk for Rent and Other Animal Tails, The Incompetent Cat and Other Animal Tails, The Duck Who Had Goosebumps and Other Animal Tails,* and *The Pint-Sized Piglet and Other Animal Tails.*

The Hopeless Hen

AND OTHER ANIMAL TAILS

edited by
GRACE FOX ANDERSON

illustrated by
Janice Skivington Wood

VICTOR BOOKS®

A DIVISION OF SCRIPTURE PRESS PUBLICATIONS INC.
USA CANADA ENGLAND

"A Boy for Sofie" previously published in *Action* by Light and Life Press, Winona Lake, IN 46590. "The Live Christmas Tree Ornament" previously published in *Discovery* by Light and Life Press. "Loudmouth" previously published in *On the Line* by Mennonite Publishing House, Scottdale, PA 15683. "Elisha's Friend," "African River Horse," "Masked Fisherman," "The World's Tallest Animal," previously published in *Story Friends* by Mennonite Publishing House. "Surprise in the Woods" previously published in *Radar* by Standard Publishing, Cincinnati, OH 45231. "Shark Bay" previously published in *Dash* by Christian Service Brigade, Wheaton, IL 60189. "Furry Fishers," "Adopted! Adopted!" "King of the Skies," "Pablo and Burrito," "Wolves on the Trail," "Betsy Doesn't Know It's Stealing," "Taller Than the Treetops," "Bingo's Accident," and "Anybody's Dog," previously published in *Counselor* by Scripture Press, 1825 College Avenue, Wheaton, IL 60187. "His Donkey Knew Best," taken with permission from *Black Gems for His Crown,* SIM International, © 1951.

Second printing, 1988

Scripture quotations are from *The Living Bible* (TLB), © 1971 by Tyndale House Publishers, Wheaton, IL and the *King James Version* (KJV). Used by permission.

Library of Congress Catalog Card Number: 87-62493
ISBN: 0-89693-452-7

VICTOR BOOKS
A division of SP Publications, Inc.
Wheaton, Illinois 60187

CONTENTS

The Hopeless Hen

A TRUE STORY
by Betty Swinford

Danny Martin and his younger sister Linda were eating lunch in the kitchen when their mother walked in, carrying a big clothes basket, and plunked it on the table.

"That chicken thinks she's a parakeet!" Mother said, laughing. "Would you believe she flew up on my shoulder and got a free ride to the clothesline?"

"I believe it," Danny said promptly. "She jumps on my shoulder too."

"Yeah," Linda put in. "Penny's a real clown. I caught her in the kitchen last week eating out of Butch's dish. But he didn't seem to mind. He was eating too, right beside her."

Just then Dad walked into the kitchen. "Clown, parakeet, or whatever," he said, "Penny's got to go."

Alarm clutched at Danny's heart and his brown eyes widened. "What do you mean, Dad?"

"That chicken is nothing but trouble. Can't keep her in the pen with the others, and she's never laid an egg in her life!" He shook his head firmly. "Penny is just not worth keeping. We're going to have her for dinner this Sunday."

"Dad! No! Give her another chance!" Danny cried.

"You can't kill Penny!" Linda shouted. "She's our pet."

"You already have a pet—Butch."

Their dog Butch thought he was being called. He trotted into the kitchen, tail wagging, ears up.

Danny smiled and patted their Chinese pug. "Not you! You're the other clown in the family." He looked up at his father. "Please, Dad, I couldn't eat Penny."

"Me neither," Linda agreed.

"Now look, kids, if you had your way, you'd make a pet out of every animal that comes along. You have one pet, and that's enough. Besides, times are hard right now. I can't afford to feed a chicken that gives nothing in return. And," he added, raising his eyebrows, "I could stand a good chicken dinner with some of your mother's homemade dumplings."

After dinner, Danny and Linda walked slowly out into the yard. Penny came running eagerly toward them, flapping her wings and squawking. In the sunlight her orange-brown feathers glowed iridescently.

"What are we going to do?" Linda wailed as Danny picked up Penny and stroked her pretty feathers.

"I don't know," Danny said, shaking his head. "Dad just doesn't understand how we feel. Maybe we should pray that he'll change his mind."

Linda brightened. "Yeah, after all, if God cares about a sparrow falling to the ground, He must care about a pet chicken!"

For the rest of that day, every time it crossed Danny's mind, he prayed. He told the Lord Jesus how he and Linda loved Penny and yet Dad needed money.

10

Each prayer he ended with, "Please help Dad to change his mind. Thanks, Lord. Amen."

The next day was Friday. With Sunday so near, Danny and Linda spent as much time as possible with Penny. She followed them around the yard, rode on their shoulders, gently took food from their fingers. And when no one was looking she skittered into the house to eat from Butch's bowl.

Several times Linda found Penny in her room, sitting on her pillow with wings neatly folded around her. Each time, Linda put Penny back outside, wondering if she'd been the guilty one who forgot to close the door.

"Dad," Danny began again on Friday night, "please don't kill Penny. She means as much to Linda and me as Butch does, and you wouldn't kill Butch."

"Danny," Mr. Martin began patiently, "Penny doesn't lay eggs, so I can't afford to keep her. Buying food for one pet is enough. Besides, she's only a chicken!"

"But—"

"I'm sorry, Danny. End of subject."

Danny sighed and stumbled from the room. When he went to bed, he couldn't sleep. He lay staring at the ceiling, trying hard to see Penny as his father did. He knew his father was having a hard time paying their bills right now, yet feeding one chicken seemed so small, especially when Penny often ate from Butch's dish. But Dad said every little bit helped. If so, then even Penny's feed did count.

After wrestling with the problem for an hour, Danny slid out of bed and knelt beside it, sighing deeply.

"Lord Jesus, I'm trying to see this the way Dad does. I know he's older so he must be right. If this is what You want, then it's OK. I know You don't always say yes to our prayers."

The next morning was Saturday. In the late afternoon, Dad would get out his hatchet, and it would all be over for Penny. But Danny knew he still wouldn't be able to eat Sunday dinner.

After lunch, he and Linda went into the yard to say good-bye to Penny. But she wasn't in the chicken pen.

"Oh, no," Danny moaned, "she must have flown over the fence again. We'd better find her before old Mr. Peabody does, or he'll be the one who has chicken for Sunday dinner."

Danny and Linda hurried through the gate and around behind the fence. They poked through weeds and around a stack of boards. "Find her?" Danny called.

"No," Linda answered. "Where do you suppose that crazy chicken has gone this time?"

"I don't know, but we've got to find her." Danny pushed back his red hair and looked around, but he couldn't see their pet chicken anywhere.

"Maybe Mr. Peabody's already caught her," Linda said. "He's threatened before to kill her if she got into his garden again."

Danny simply grunted. Any minute he expected Penny to come clucking toward him, then fly onto his shoulder for a ride home. But she didn't appear.

"What are we going to do?" Linda cried.

Danny shrugged. "Go home, I guess. Maybe she'll come back on her own."

As they walked back into their own yard, both children stopped, their mouths open in horror. Dad was walking toward the house, carrying a freshly killed chicken.

"Daddy!" Linda screamed.

Danny steeled himself against the quick onrush of tears.

Mr. Martin put out his free hand. "Hold on, kids! This isn't Penny!"

Linda's mouth dropped even more. "It's not?" she asked, wonderingly.

"No, there's Penny over there. She's fine."

"But—I—thought," Danny broke off, wondering what had happened to change his father's mind.

"Penny saved her neck just in time," Mr. Martin said, smiling. "Ask your mother."

They dashed into the house calling, "Mom! Mom! Why did Dad change his mind about killing Penny? Where has she been?"

Mother led them to Linda's room and pointed toward the bed. "That's where Penny's been. Look at your pillow, Linda."

Linda and Danny both rushed over to the bed. There on Linda's pillow lay a large, shiny white egg!

Anybody's Dog

A FICTION STORY
by Madeleine P. Birch

"Come here, Duke!" Shawn called. His dalmatian turned and looked at his young master. He wagged his tail and seemed to be laughing.

"Come here, Duke!" Mark called from his place beside Shawn on a park bench. Duke ran over to the blond boy to be patted. "See—he obeys me better than he does you," Mark said, grinning, as he pulled on Duke's ears.

"Yes, I know." Shawn pretended to groan. "He's anybody's dog." The two boys were still sitting there, playing with Duke when the new boy in the neighborhood walked by with his fine German shepherd close at his heels.

Duke pricked up his ears and quivered. "No, Duke," Mark said. Duke put his ears back as if he were ashamed, and wagged his friendly tail. But his eyes followed the German shepherd until the boy and his dog were out of sight.

"German shepherds are one-man dogs," Mark said.

"You should make Duke more of a one-man dog."

"Duke?" Shawn asked, laughing. "It can't be done. He's too friendly." Shawn kicked gently at his dog who playfully grabbed the boy's shoestring. Duke was well-known in town because everyone saved scraps for him. It seemed that everyone knew Duke.

As the boys walked slowly home, Mark remarked, "That new boy is sure to enter his dog in the Scout Dog Show next week. We'd better get busy and go over those obedience tests with Duke again."

Shawn laughed. "That's easy. Anyone can teach Duke anything."

"Yeah," Mark answered quickly, "that's just the trouble. In the dog show, it's the dog's master who has to make him obey."

"Guess I can do it if I have to. I only wish the German shepherd wasn't such a good dog—or didn't have such a good master." Shawn was thinking out loud.

"Yeah, but that new kid is always alone. He looks like he could use some friends," Mark said.

Shawn nodded.

The boys were sure Duke could take high honors at the dog show as far as his looks were concerned. He was built beautifully and his white coat with black spots shone after a good brushing. But they were worried about the obedience tests.

On Shawn's front lawn, they taught Duke to walk beside them so closely that he curved his body to fit their legs. They taught him to jump over the low badminton net and to "sit" until given a hand signal to move.

By the end of the week, Shawn and Mark had Duke trained in the obedience tests required in the dog show. That is, all the tests but one. When they made a pile of things such as balls, gloves, shoes, car keys, and other things belonging to the family, and told Duke to "Get," he was bewildered. He couldn't seem to learn to "get" just the shoe belonging to Shawn.

Wagging his tail Duke brought everything to Shawn. When scolded, he brought the things to Mark, one by one. When scolded again, Duke tilted his head sideways as if to say, "I don't understand."

"See?" Shawn said. "He *is* anybody's dog. He'll never win the blue ribbon for best dog in the show against that one-man German shepherd." Shawn shook his head hopelessly at Duke.

Duke didn't care. He leaped up and snatched Shawn's cap from his head and loped across the lawn, with the boys shouting and running after him.

Day after day, the boys tried to teach Duke to pick Shawn's shoe from a pile of things on the lawn. Day after day, Duke brought every item in the pile to either Shawn or Mark.

The day before the dog show Shawn, Mark, and Duke relaxed on the lawn. Duke pricked up his ears and dashed toward the new boy and his German shepherd dog, coming down the street.

The German shepherd walked along beside his master, grumbling a deep throaty growl at the dalmatian. But Duke wagged his tail and sniffed at the other dog in a friendly way.

"Hi," Shawn called to the boy. "You're Cam, aren't you?"

The boy just looked at Shawn and walked on.

"Let's see your dog do a retrieving trick," Mark called.

Cam stopped, glanced at the pile of things on the lawn, and told his dog to heel. When he told the dog to sit, he sat. Then Cam walked over to the heap and put his ring under the pile.

Back at the dog's side, he ordered, "Major, get." Quickly, his dog nuzzled the heap, found the ring, and brought it to his master.

"Say, that's some dog!" Shawn said.

"And well trained," added Mark.

"Want to bat a few balls with us?" Shawn asked.

Cam looked startled. "Ah—no, thanks," he stammered, and started down the street as if he were in a hurry.

Shawn looked at Mark. "What's wrong with him?"

Mark shrugged. "Like dog, like master. I guess he is a one-dog boy. But I still think he's lonely."

The next day at the dog show, Major and Duke ran neck and neck for top honors. Major was a fine show dog, but he would let no one touch him except Cam.

The last test was the trick that Mark and Shawn could not teach Duke. Duke walked up to the heap and brought the first thing on top back to Shawn. But Major brought the gold ring to Cam promptly.

At that point, Shawn was sure Major had won the blue ribbon. And he was right. After the show, Shawn and Mark found Cam and congratulated him on having the best dog in the show. Cam smiled and thanked them.

"Want to walk home with us?" Mark asked. "It's a long walk to take alone."

"Sure," Cam answered. This time he seemed friendlier.

As they left the Scout Camp, Duke tried to make friends with Major, but it was not until Cam ordered him to be friendly that Major would wag his tail and stop growling.

As the boys and their dogs walked together, Cam told them he didn't make friends easily because his family was always moving. "My parents bought me Major when I was

17

little because I was alone so much. Now Major and I are always together. And that's why he won't obey anyone but me."

Cam motioned to Major with his hand. When the boy did so, he stopped and stared. "Wow! My ring! I left it at the dog show!" he cried.

"Was it valuable?" Mark asked, wondering if the ring could be found in the growing dusk of the fall afternoon.

"Sure was! It belonged to my dad!" Cam said. "I've got to get it back."

"Come, Major!" he called, and started to run back toward the scout camp.

"Wait!" Shawn shouted. "You don't want to walk all the way home alone, do you?"

But Cam ran on, his dog beside him.

"It's three miles home," Mark said to Shawn, "and he may not know the way. Shouldn't we go back with him?"

Shawn wasn't listening. "Here, Duke!" he called. Duke came loping to his side. Then Shawn called, "Cam, come back! I have an idea."

This time Cam stopped and trotted back to the other boys.

Shawn dug in his jeans pocket and pulled out a stubby pencil and scrap of paper. "Look," he said, "I'll send Duke back to Mr. Woods, the scoutmaster with this note in his collar. Mr. Woods lives near the camp. Major won't obey anyone but you, will he?"

"No," Cam said, shaking his head miserably.

"Well, tell Major to follow Duke. Will he do that?" Shawn asked.

"Yes, if I say so," Cam said.

"Duke will obey Mr. Woods and Major will get your ring. They'll be back in no time."

Cam let Major sniff his finger where the ring had been. "Go get!" he ordered.

Shawn said to Duke, "Go see Mr. Woods!"

"Follow Duke," Cam ordered Major.

But Major sat down and cocked his head at Cam until Cam patted Duke's head and said, "Nice dog. Follow Duke."

"Go get," Shawn said as he pointed up the road.

Duke went off like a streak, and at another word from his master, Major followed.

The boys waited fifteen minutes before the dogs came bounding back. Major held the ring in his teeth and dropped it in his grateful master's hand. Duke had a note from Mr. Woods.

"Duke is anybody's dog," read the note. "He didn't bring the note to me, but to my wife. She's the one who saves bones for him. Major wouldn't hunt for the ring in the dark until I told Duke to go get a handkerchief I had dropped. Duke brought both the ring and the handkerchief. Then we almost had a dog fight because Major tried to get the ring. I took it out of Duke's mouth and gave it to Major. I'll put this note on Duke's collar. Now hurry home."

The boys crowded together under a streetlight to read the note. On the way home, Major found it hard to be friendly to anyone but Cam. Yet when Cam nodded, Major let Shawn and Mark pet him.

At this point, Cam begged Shawn to take the blue ribbon for best dog in the show. "Duke is the best dog in the world," Cam insisted.

"Forget it," Shawn said, laughing. "As soon as you teach Major to make friends with people, he'll be the best dog in the world."

"I'll teach him to play with Duke," Cam said.

"How about coming over to the park and playing ball with us tomorrow?" Mark asked as they neared home, a weary trio.

"I'd sure like to," Cam said.

"And how about Bible club on Saturday?" Shawn asked.

"Sure," Cam agreed.

Shawn and Mark watched Cam and his dog go down the street. "Well, he sure warmed up fast, didn't he?" Mark said.

"Like dog, like boy," Shawn answered. "Come here, Duke." Duke was following Major down the street.

"Come, Duke. Come here!" Mark called. And Duke came running.

"Anybody's old dog, aren't you, Dukey?" said both boys together, each one fondling a black ear.

"HE'S MORE LIKE HIS OLD SELF ALREADY."

Beast of
the Old Testament

by Gloria A. Truitt

I'm that growly *king of beasts*
    Who wears a furry mane.
The Jordan Valley was my home,
    And there I used to reign.
When Daniel *safely* spent a night,
    Imprisoned in my den,
He bravely proved God's power to
    A group of jealous men.
What animal am I who roamed
    The thickets 'round old Zion,
And stalked the shepherds' sheep and goats?
    Of course, I'm called the lion!

Daniel 6:16-24

Emily's "Magic" Pet

A TRUE STORY
by Ragene Henry

"It's not fair! Emily gets everything because she's older," Susan grumbled.

"You know that's not true," Mom said. "Emily worked hard to get her guinea pig. She earned it."

Susan knew that. She remembered the many evenings and Saturdays Emily had worked on her project for the Sunday School fair instead of playing or watching TV. And she had been proud and happy when Emily was awarded a gift certificate for the miniature Bible scene she'd made. But Susan was not happy now as Emily talked about her new pet.

"I think I'll name her Pixie," Emily said. "Isn't that a good name, Susan?"

Susan didn't answer.

Mom laughed. "Pixie is a funny name for a guinea pig that's so chubby," she said.

"It's a dumb name for a dumb pet for a dumb sister," Susan mumbled to herself. "And I'm never going to speak

22

to her or play with her again for as long as I live."

Susan sat in the recliner, chewing on her hair ribbon and watching Emily rush around. Emily was busily making a new home for Pixie in a large box lined with wood shavings from Daddy's workshop.

In one corner of the box, Emily tied the special water bottle from the pet store. In another corner, she placed a shoe box for Pixie's private little sleeping room.

Then Emily went to the refrigerator and took the outside leaves of a head of lettuce. Placing these in Pixie's box, Emily said, "Here's your first supper in your new home, Pixie."

I hope Pixie chokes on the lettuce, Susan grumped silently.

"Do you want to hold her, Susan?" Emily asked.

"No way!" Susan said, forgetting for a minute that she was never going to speak to Emily again. But then she remembered and she stomped to her room, slamming the door behind her.

For five days Susan remembered that she was never going to speak to Emily or play with her again. It wasn't always easy. In fact, Susan got bored playing just with her dolls and began to feel lonely.

Whenever she saw Emily playing with her guinea pig— talking to Pixie and feeding her—Susan felt hurt, angry, and left out. *It's always just Emily and Pixie now,* Susan thought. *Emily's so busy with her dumb old guinea pig that she doesn't even notice I'm not talking to her. I wish Pixie would die.*

But Susan's thoughts did not make her any happier.

Then Friday, after school, Susan and Emily ran into the house and threw their backpacks over the hooks by the door. As usual, Emily went straight to Pixie's box to say hello.

Susan stood back by the door, listening for the happy squeaky sounds Pixie made. But today she heard nothing. She inched closer to get a better look as Emily crouched down, reaching for her pet.

Pixie squealed. It was a sound of pain and fear.

Emily looked up at Susan. "Something's wrong with Pixie. I think she's sick."

"Mom!" Emily called as she ran off to find Mother.

Susan bent down and looked closely at the ball of soft white fur huddled in a corner of the box. "Please don't be sick. Please don't die, Pixie. We love you," she said softly.

Susan closed her eyes and whispered, "Dear Lord Jesus, please don't let Pixie die. I didn't really mean all those bad things I thought. Honest. Please forgive me and help Pixie to get well."

Mother called the pet store.

"Keep her warm," the pet store owner said. "Make sure she gets plenty of water. She'll probably be OK by morning."

Emily and Susan spent the night in their sleeping bags on the floor beside Pixie's box. They planned to stay awake all night, taking care of the guinea pig. They fed her water from a turkey baster, and Susan even lent Pixie her favorite blanket, the one with the chewed satin edges.

As the night got later, Pixie seemed to get quieter. Soon Emily and Susan got quieter too and fell asleep.

It seemed as though she had just closed her eyes when the sunlight streaming in the window, danced on Susan's face and woke her up. Her first thought was of Pixie.

Slipping out of her sleeping bag, she knelt beside the box and looked for her sister's pet. But she couldn't see the little animal anywhere. "Oh, no!" she said out loud, waking Emily.

Emily jumped up, her sleeping bag falling down around her legs. "What's the matter? Is Pixie OK?"

"I don't know. She's not here," Susan said.

"She's got to be there!" Emily looked into the box. Then she reached in and lifted up the shoe-box room. There was Pixie. Emily traced her fingers carefully down the guinea pig's back, and Pixie squeaked in her usual happy way.

Susan breathed a sigh of relief. "Thank You, Jesus," she said out loud. Then she and Emily looked at each other and smiled.

"I guess she's OK this morning," Emily said happily, as Mom joined the girls.

"She's better than OK," Mom said, laughing. "Look more closely."

Emily and Susan peered into the box. "What's this?" Emily asked as she nudged Pixie and saw a tiny ball of fur, snuggled beside her pet.

"It's a baby!" Susan cried.

"A beautiful tiny baby guinea pig," Emily said, as she began to jump up and down. "No wonder Pixie was so chubby. She was going to have a baby. Susan, isn't it great? The baby can be yours. Now we'll each have a guinea pig. OK?"

Susan began to jump up and down with Emily. "OK!" she shouted. It was great to have such a terrific sister with such a terrific "magic" pet and such a wonderful Lord Jesus who listens to kids' prayers.

The Bear Out There

A TRUE STORY
by Jennie Johnson

"**S**urprise!" Mother announced when she woke up Cindy and me early one Saturday morning. "We're going to the mountains for a picnic today."

My younger sister and I jumped out of our beds and dressed quickly. I helped Cindy brush her blond hair while Mother packed our lunch. When Mother was done, Father put the picnic basket in the trunk of the car and we headed toward the Chiricahau Mountains, about thirty miles from our home in Tucson, Arizona.

Gradually, the desert floor gave way to cedar and juniper trees. The air began to feel cooler as we drove up into the mountains. Cindy spotted a red fox slinking through a clump of scrubby oaks and Mother pointed out two mule deer high on a hillside.

"There are several old mines tucked away in these mountains," Father said. "We might even find an old log cabin or two still standing."

Cindy, about eight then, frowned. "Wouldn't miners be

scared to live way up here—with all the wild animals?"

Mother looked thoughtful. "Well, not if they put their trust in Jesus. Remember, living in the city can be dangerous too. Everyone needs to trust the Lord, no matter where they may live."

"You mean because God is everywhere, He can protect us anywhere?" Cindy asked.

"That's right," Mother agreed. "Look," she pointed up the hillside. "There's an old mine right there."

Father stopped the car and we all jumped out. "Careful!" he warned. "Some of these mine aren't very safe. They could cave in at any time so let's take it slow."

He shone his flashlight into the dark opening in the side of the hill and saw that the beams supporting the roof of a long tunnel were in good shape. Pieces of old railing for the ore carts still lined the floor.

"This must be an old gold mine," he said. "Usually there's a shaft somewhere that goes almost straight up through the roof to the outside."

Cindy and I followed Mother and Father into the dark tunnel. A musty odor filled the mine. From somewhere ahead, I could hear water dripping. I shivered in the cool air. About thirty feet into the mine the tunnel divided into three branches.

"We don't want to get lost," Father warned. "We'd better wait till after lunch to explore farther. Then I'll bring a piece of rope and tie it to the main tunnel. That way we can follow the rope down a branch without getting lost."

Back at the car, Mother spread out an old tablecloth on the ground. After thanking the Lord for the roast beef sandwiches, freshly baked cookies, and lemonade Mother had prepared, we ate until full. Afterward, I leaned back against a pine tree. Gazing around, I spotted a log cabin half-hidden from view on the steep hillside near us.

"Look, Cindy!" I cried. "Let's go check out that cabin."

"All right," Father agreed. "Mother and I will explore the mine some more while you two take a look. Just be careful."

My sister led the way up the hillside. The cabin was farther than we'd thought and the climb was steep. Our faces were red and we were gasping for breath when we finally reached the weathered, old building.

The one-room cabin was falling apart. The door was broken off its hinges and leaned crookedly against the opening. Its one window had no trace of screen or glass.

We entered cautiously and looked around. The floor was made of packed dirt and littered with old cans and dusty sacks of what appeared to be oatmeal and grains. I noticed that several of the burlap sacks had been ripped and torn by an animal of some sort.

Suddenly Cindy grabbed my arm. "Jennie," she whispered, "I think I hear something out there."

Then I heard it too and froze. It sounded like a large animal crashing through the thick underbrush and heading toward us. But I said, "It must be Mother and Father."

We ran to the open window opening and peered out just as a large brown bear broke through the bushes about twenty feet away and ambled toward the cabin. Cindy's eyes widened in terror and she opened her mouth to scream.

"Oh, Jesus, please don't let that bear come in here," I prayed aloud. "Show us that You *are* everywhere and You see that bear too."

Cindy closed her mouth and reached for my hand. We watched out the open window as the bear rounded the far corner of the cabin. In another minute it would surely find the open door behind us.

If only Mother and Father hadn't gone back in the tunnel, I thought. I knew it would be impossible for them to hear us if we shouted for help. Only Jesus could hear us now.

Then I suddenly remembered reading somewhere that bears are afraid of loud noises. I grabbed a rusty saucepan and beat it hard against the wall. Cindy followed my lead and began singing at the top of her lungs.

A dark blur crossed the open doorway as the startled bear dashed up the hillside. We raced out of the cabin and stumbled down the hill in the opposite direction. Reaching the car, we stopped and held our aching sides as we looked around to be sure the bear hadn't followed us.

"Wow!" Cindy cried. "I thought we'd had it, Jennie."

"Me too," I admitted.

"I guess Jesus really is with us all the time, isn't He?" she said thoughtfully.

Happy tears filled my eyes and I nodded. "He sure is!"

Just then Mother and Father ducked out of the mine nearby. "Wait'll I tell you what we saw in there, girls," Mother called.

Cindy grinned at me. "Wait till you hear what we saw, Mother," she answered.

Elisha's Friend

by Gloria A. Truitt

Elisha was the victim of
  A group of jeering boys,
So I attacked them with my claws
  And growled a growly noise!

No longer do I roam the hills
  And woods of Israel,
But long ago in Bible times
  That's where I used to dwell.

Elisha's Friend

I was the shepherd's enemy.
   Their baby lambs I'd stalk,
For when I was quite hungry,
   I would steal one from the flock.

My teeth and claws are long and sharp,
   A shaggy coat I wear!
By now I'm sure you've guessed my name.
   I'm Mister Growly Bear!

2 Kings 2:23-24

Furry Fishers

A NATURE STORY
by Joan Pollard Cohen

Mr. Logan, the forest ranger, pointed to the trees ahead. "Just over that ridge is where I spotted the mother bear and her cub last week. We may see them there today."

Ten-year-old Scott was both excited and scared. Reading about how to stalk bears was one thing. Doing it was something else!

He and his parents were in Colorado on vacation. At church the day before, they had met Mr. Logan, a forest ranger in that area. When Scott told him he wanted to get some photos for his Stockade Club nature badge, Mr. Logan had offered to take him on a hike to see some black bears.

"Keep low and quiet," cautioned Ranger Logan. "We don't want the mother bear to get our scent. She and the cubs might run off. In fact, if she thinks her cubs are in danger, she might even charge us. The Bible speaks of being 'as upset as a mother bear who has been robbed of her cubs' (2 Sam. 17:8, TLB). We certainly don't want to

get her angry now, do we?" he asked, grinning.

Scott crept silently after the ranger. When they reached the bushes near the stream, they hid in them and waited. A sudden movement downstream caught their attention. "There they are," said the ranger quietly. Scott strained to see. Sure enough, the large black bear and her cub were right in the water, coming toward them.

The animals' coats glistened in the sunlight. Suddenly, the mother bear reached down into the stream and in one swipe brought up a struggling salmon.

"She's got a fish!" Scott exclaimed and reached for his camera. The photos of the bears would be a great addition to the report he was writing for the badge.

"Salmon is one of their favorite meals," the ranger commented.

"Now the cub has one," whispered Scott, as the mother flipped a fish out of the water and into the cub's paws in one motion.

"It won't be long before junior is as skilled a fisherman as his mother," said Mr. Logan. "His mother is a good teacher."

"Hey, I've got a good view of them in my camera," Scott said as he snapped a picture. "My telephoto lens brings them real close."

Scott took more pictures, and finally Mr. Logan said they'd have to head back to the lodge where Scott was staying with his folks. As they walked, he gave Scott a rundown on bears.

"The young ones are born while the mother is hibernating in the winter," he began. "They're hairless and blind and weigh only eight or nine pounds. A couple of months later, when they leave the den, they are furry little rascals about the size of a grown raccoon.

"The mother black bear has from two to four cubs every other year—a good thing, since it takes two years for them to grow up, and she has all the work of raising them. She teaches them how to hunt and fish and care for themselves."

"They eat almost anything, don't they?" Scott asked. "Like berries and honey as well as fish?"

"Yes, in that way at least, their diet is like ours," Mr. Logan agreed. "God, in His wisdom, has given the bear a natural cunning and intelligence—also a love of fun," Mr. Logan continued.

"And, you know, cubs are just like little children. They think life is all fun and play. One time I watched two small cubs climb a young tree until their weight bent it to the ground. They jumped off and ran right back up the tree and did it again."

Scott laughed. "I've read about trained bears that do

tricks," he said.

"Yes, black bears are real clowns," Mr. Logan said, shaking his head as if remembering. "Even in the wild, they stand on their heads and turn somersaults over and over. But remember, bears are not to be played *with*."

Scott looked puzzled.

"They have quick tempers," Mr. Logan explained. "They'll tear apart anything or anyone that gets in the way when they're angry. That's why we tell tourists not to feed wild bears.

"Besides, a bear has tremendous strength. He can take off your head with a swipe of a paw. He's fast too, and a good climber."

Scott nodded. "While driving up here, we saw a bear chase a man. The man was trying to take a picture. He hardly had time to get back to his car."

The ranger and boy were near the lodge now, so Scott thanked Mr. Logan for taking him to see the mother bear and cub out in the woods. "Thanks loads, Mr. Logan. That was neat! I'll send you some prints of my photos if they turn out good."

"Sure thing, Scott," Mr. Logan said, smiling. "I'm sure you'll have a good report to turn in for that nature badge."

A Boy for Sofie

A TRUE STORY
by Jane C. Foss

"Feed me tender, feed me true, feed me something new," crooned the voice on the TV set as a baby basset hound, holding its dish in its mouth, looked out with sorrowful, drooping eyes.

"Mom, can I please have a dog?" Kyle pleaded as he danced around the kitchen, trying to get his mother's attention. "Every boy should have a dog. I'd feed it myself, walk it, and take care of it. Please, Mom!"

"Kyle, please get out of my way. Dad will be here in just a few minutes, and I have to get dinner started. He has an early meeting this evening." She balanced cucumbers and a head of lettuce in one hand and a tomato and onion in the other.

"If I had a dog, I wouldn't be in here getting in your way. I'd be outside playing with him."

"Kyle, honey," his mother said as she put down the salad makings and put her hands on his shoulders. "We can't have a dog. We're gone all day. Since I've been working, I don't have the energy to train a puppy. Besides, it isn't fair to leave a puppy alone all day. He'd have to be shut in the kitchen or basement."

"But I'd train him. And I could come home at lunchtime to play with him."

"Kyle, you know what happened when you had the goldfish and the turtle."

"But dogs are different. Dogs are friends."

"Well, they still have to be fed every day, not just once a week or whenever you remember. And they have to be taken outside often when they're little. A puppy is like a baby, Kyle."

Mother hugged her ten-year-old son close to her. "I wish I could say 'yes' to you, but I can't. And even if I did, your father wouldn't agree. You know he doesn't like animals in the house. Now please don't make things any harder for me. Be an angel, please, and set the table." She gave him a gentle shove toward the small, adjoining dining area.

As he placed the plates and silverware on the table, Kyle thought about last week's Sunday School lesson. *God always hears our prayers. He knows what we need and want most. He doesn't always answer the way we want or expect, but He is a loving God.*

"God, I sure hope You're listening to my prayer for a dog," Kyle whispered.

After dinner, he went out to ride his bike for a while before bedtime. The April evenings were getting longer, and the early evening air held a faint promise of the warm weather to come.

"Hi, Kyle." Mrs. Roberts waved from her porch next door. Kyle rode his bike up her driveway. He often stopped to talk with Mr. or Mrs. Roberts. Their children were grown up and away somewhere, and Mrs. Roberts always seemed to have time to listen to Kyle talk about his school day or his friends.

"Are you going to play ball this summer, Kyle?" Mrs. Roberts asked. "We enjoyed watching your games last summer."

"I'm going to be trying out next week. Will you really come to watch me play?"

"If the time is right. We miss doing things like that with our boys now that they're grown up. Be sure to let us know how your tryouts go."

"Sure will," Kyle said as he jumped on his bike and sped down the driveway. "Gotta go now and finish my homework. See you tomorrow."

Several weeks later as Kyle rode his bike to school one morning, he saw Mrs. Roberts walking around her front yard. He started to call to her but suddenly slammed on his brakes and stared into her yard. Mrs. Roberts was holding a red strap and it was attached to—Kyle couldn't believe his eyes—a basset hound puppy.

Kyle rushed over to get acquainted. The puppy's ears were so long that she stepped on them and tumbled over. Her white-tipped tail wagged as she looked up at Kyle with the mournful eyes of the TV dog.

"Where did you get him? Whose is he? How did you know? What's his name?" The questions tumbled out.

"Her name is Sofie. We got her yesterday. She's ten weeks old and what do you mean 'how did I know'?"

"That I wanted a basset hound."

"I didn't. But I did know how much *I* wanted one. I've always wanted a basset hound, so Mr. Roberts bought me one for my birthday."

Kyle lay down on the grass, his face close to the little

dog. A pink tongue brushed his cheek. Kyle giggled. "She's so cute. Look at those ears. She's walking on them. And those eyes." He sat cross-legged and picked up the wriggling animal. "Do you think she likes me?"

"I'm sure of it. Look at her. She's wagging her whole body, not just her tail."

"I love her already, but I have to go now. I'll see you later, Sofie. May I come and see her this afternoon?" Kyle asked.

"Of course," Mrs. Roberts said. "I'll need you to help me with her. Every dog should have a boy, and since I don't have one of my own here anymore, I'd like it if you would be Sofie's boy. That is, if you want to."

"Mrs. Roberts, I'd be happy to be Sofie's boy. I'll come everyday after school and take her for a walk. I'll teach her tricks, and if you ever need someone to look after her while you go away, I'll be glad to do that."

39

"It's a deal, Kyle. I think Sofie needs a nap now and you'd better dash for school. We'll both be expecting you later this afternoon." Mrs. Roberts picked up the puppy and headed toward the house. With a happy smile and a wave, Kyle ran to his bike.

As he pedaled up the hill toward school he thought to himself, *God sure does answer prayers in unexpected ways. A basset hound puppy next door is almost as good as having my own. This is going to be a great summer!*

Loudmouth

A NATURE STORY
by June Eaton

"There's the campground, Dad!" Dave cried. He held onto his seat as the car bounced along the old gravel road toward Deep Ridge Campground. Dad pulled into a small clearing surrounded by tall, fragrant pines. While he and Dave set up the tent, Mother unpacked the food.

Soon they had a good fire going, and Dave shoved a hot dog onto the end of a stick. "I like them when they burst their skins," he said, as he watched the juicy dog turn to scorched brown.

"Just wait till tomorrow," Dad said. "We'll be sinking our teeth into those fish we're going to catch!" Dave stared at the flames and dreamed about the rainbow trout they'd pull out of the lake in the morning. Then as the sky turned to a dusky purple, the family held hands and prayed there beside the fire.

"This is the nicest time of all," sighed Dave. The Lord seemed very near.

Dad broke the spell when he doused the campfire.

"We'd better turn in, Dave," he said. "Best fishing is early in the morning, you know."

Dave washed up in the icy spring water and eased into his sleeping bag. "Good night, Mom. Good night, Dad," he whispered above the familiar cricket symphony.

Suddenly, from high up in the trees came another sound—a loud sound that was new to Dave. *A bird, probably,* he thought. The three whistled notes sounded over and over again. Dave turned in his sleeping bag and tried to concentrate on sleep. But those three notes kept sounding over and over again.

"What is that noise?" Dave called to his parents.

"Sounds as if he's saying, 'Whip-poor-will,'" said Dad. "Go to sleep, Son."

Dave tried again, this time lying on his back. But the bird started up again with his "Whip-poor-will, whip-poor-will, whip-poor-will," over and over and over again.

"Doesn't he ever quit?" Dave asked his father. But Dad was fast asleep.

"He makes that sound while he's flying around, hunting for food," Mother said quietly. "He'll probably get his fill soon."

But the bird didn't stop whistling, so Dave found some cotton for his ears in the first-aid kit. But that didn't help, so he put his pillow over his head and dug deeper into his sleeping bag. "That bird must eat all night long! Quiet, you loudmouth!" he muttered.

The next thing Dave knew, faint streams of light were trickling through the tent and both Mom's and Dad's sleeping bags were empty. Dave jumped up and pulled on his jeans, then hurried out to the campfire. Mom was huddled close to it, finishing a cup of coffee and looking at her bird book.

"Where's Dad?" Dave asked.

"Oh, good morning, Dear," she answered. "He went fishing. He's probably on the other side of the lake by now."

"But why didn't he call me?" Dave cried.

"We both tried to wake you up, but you didn't even stir. Dad said if you were that tired, we'd better let you sleep."

Dave kicked a stone into the fire. "Aw, it was that loud-mouthed bird! He made so much noise I couldn't sleep."

Mom laughed. "You mean that whippoorwill? It says here in my book that his scientific name is *Caprimulgus vociferus*. Vociferous means 'crying out loudly,' so I guess he's well-named."

"You see?" Dave said. "I told you he was a loudmouth."

"He sleeps during the day," Mother went on.

"That figures," Dave said. "He'll sleep all day so he can keep me awake all night!"

Mother chuckled and kept on reading. "He rarely flies except when feeding. His drab brown and gray colors blend in with the dead leaves, so he's almost invisible when resting on the ground."

"Lucky for him. He probably has lots of enemies!" Dave poured himself some milk from the cooler, then ate a big bowl of cereal. "When will Dad be back?"

"Probably not till lunchtime," Mother said.

"Oh, no," Dave groaned. "That dumb bird made me miss fishing with Dad for a whole morning. I'm going to do something about that!" He rummaged around in his dad's equipment box, then poked around the woods for sticks and vines. "How big did you say that bird was, Mom?"

"About the size of a robin. Why? What are you doing?"

"I'm making a trap. I'm going to catch that monster and put him in a cage. You said he whistles only when he's flying, so if he can't fly he can't make that awful racket."

"But if he doesn't fly, he doesn't eat," Mom reminded him. "You wouldn't want to starve him to death. He's one of God's creatures, you know."

"No, I just want to keep him quiet. Couldn't I feed him?" Dave asked.

"I'm afraid you couldn't begin to satisfy his appetite. You said yourself he has a big mouth. That's for catching lots and LOTS of food. Besides, wild animals aren't meant to be caged."

Dave tossed aside the makings of his trap. He rested his chin on his knees and thought some more. Soon Dad returned with a string of beautiful rainbow trout.

"Wow, Dad! What a catch!" Dave exclaimed. "Are you going back again later? Can I go with you? Are you going to take the boat out?"

"Whoa! Hold on!" Dad said. "I think that's all the fishing for today. Mom wants to take a hike and look for wild flowers. Maybe we can end up with a swim." Dave nodded and tried to hide his disappointment.

As they hiked through the woods, Dave's mind was still on the whippoorwill. Soon they passed a cornfield on the edge of the woods. "I've got it!" Dave shouted. "I know what to do about that bird!" After the hike, he gathered some old clothes and began stuffing them with grass.

"What on earth?" Dad looked puzzled.

"A scarecrow, Dad," Dave said. "If it can keep crows away, maybe it will keep the whippoorwill away so I can get some sleep tonight."

Dave set up the scarecrow on a small sapling. When they came back from swimming, Mom got the fish frying in the pan. It was beginning to get dark as they finished eating.

"We've had a full day," Dad said.

"Yeah, but no fishing," Dave grumbled. He slapped at a mosquito on his arm.

Mom was waving her arms around her head. "Oh, these pesky insects!" she cried. "I didn't notice them last night."

"Probably Dave's scarecrow is working after all," Dad observed. He winked at Mother.

"What do you mean, Dad? Scarecrows don't frighten insects." Dave laughed at Dad's joke.

"No, but if it did scare away the whippoorwill, then you've got more bugs. All the while that bird is flying around, making noise, he's cutting down the insect population. That's part of God's plan to keep a balance in nature."

"Awwk—!" Dave cried out, as a swarm of tiny insects flew into his mouth and ears. "Let me out of here!" He jumped up and ran over to the scarecrow and pulled it down.

Later, as he crawled into his sleeping bag and prayed, he could hear the whippoorwill warming up for another concert. "Ooooh!" Dave complained. "Another night of this!"

"Dave," Mom called. "Why don't you try counting sheep. That's Grandpa's favorite remedy for not falling asleep."

Dave grunted. He rolled over and pulled the cotton from his ears. "I know what I'll do. I'll count the number of times that loudmouthed bird says, "Whippoorwill."

Mom and Dad laughed as he began counting.

"One, two, three—I wonder how long he'll go on without stopping—four, five, six, seven, eight-t-t-z-z-z-z-."

Adopted! Adopted!

A FICTION STORY
by Mel Boring

"**B**rian had always known it. His parents had told him from the time he was old enough to understand the word. But then it had only been a word. *Adopted.* Now he understood more than just the word, and being adopted had become a big ache inside. He felt that being adopted made him different from other kids.

And they seemed to know how he felt. Whenever they were angry with him, they flung the word like a poison dart, "Adopted, adopted. Brian McGraw's adopted!"

Today he just couldn't bear their teasing. When school let out, he took a new route home to avoid them. *Adopted means my real parents didn't want me,* he moaned to himself. *I don't really belong to anybody.*

Soon he found himself on an unfamiliar street. The houses were taller than those in his neighborhood and they were joined together. He stared up at the tall buildings, not watching his feet.

A sudden "A-i-i-e-e!" from under his feet made him

jump. Startled, he looked down at a bundle of fur that measured halfway to his knees. He could tell by the wagging tail that it was a puppy. "I'm sorry, little guy," Brian apologized, picking up the puppy. "Let's look at that foot."

From the way the puppy licked Brian's face, it appeared that he had forgotten about his paw.

"You're a friendly stranger," Brian said, laughing. He wasn't sure the dog even had eyes until he brushed the hair up and peered into two chocolate spots. They were as friendly as the wagging tail.

Warmed by the friendly little animal, Brian forgot for a moment where he was. He even forgot he was adopted.

Suddenly, Brian realized he had to get home. "It'll be suppertime, little puppy," he said sadly, as he lowered the dog to the ground and hurried toward home. Two blocks later he was waiting impatiently for a red light when he felt something brush against his legs. The puppy!

"Go home, Boy!" Brian shouted, trying his best to be stern.

Finally the dog disappeared into the blur of row houses, and Brian trudged home.

It had been good to forget awhile about being adopted. But now Brian began to think about it again. *Why didn't my real parents want me?*

As he started up the steps of his house, he groaned. A now familiar pitter-patter of puppy paws stopped when he stopped. Brian plopped down on the top step and the puppy hopped into his lap. He was just telling the dog he couldn't stay when the door opened. It was his mother.

"Where were you, Brian?" she asked. "I was worried about you."

"I just went for a walk," Brian said without looking up.

"What's that in your lap? Oh, isn't he cute!" Mother

exclaimed, bending down to pet the dog.

As Brian explained where the dog had come from, he realized that Mother might let him keep the puppy. She seemed to like the little dog.

"No," his mother replied when he asked. "We don't have room for a dog here in the city. Besides, he belongs to someone else, and it wouldn't be right to keep him. You'd better take him back home quickly before your father comes home for supper."

Disappointed, Brian started back to where he'd met his new friend. "I'll never get a dog!" he grumbled to the puppy. "I'll bet if I wasn't adopted, I would! Maybe I just won't go back home!"

But after dropping the pup into a fenced yard near their meeting place, Brian did return home. He ate supper silently. Finally, he excused himself and dragged to his room.

The next morning when Brian came to breakfast, he was surprised to see the puppy in the kitchen.

"He scratched at the door last night after you went to bed, Brian," his mother explained. "We couldn't sleep, so your father let him in. He said you're to take him back after school tonight and find his owner so he'll stay home." That ended Brian's short-lived hope.

After school Brian began knocking on the doors of the tall houses where he had found the puppy. Everyone who answered his knock said the dog wasn't his. In fact, one woman yelled, "No, he's not ours, so don't leave him here!"

"You're such a cute little puppy. I can't understand why no one wants you," Brian told the dog. "I'd sure like to have you, but Mom and Dad say no. I guess I'd better get home now."

He gently set the dog down behind a fence and started home. As he looked back over his shoulder one last time at the pup's pleading eyes, he thought suddenly of the story he had heard the day he became a Christian.

It was about the one lonely sheep who had gotten away from the ninety-nine others. Brian wished he could reach out and comfort the lonely pup as the Lord Jesus had reached out that day and comforted him.

"Just in time for supper," Brian's mother called as he opened the door.

"Did you find the pup's home?" his father asked as they pulled their chairs up to the table.

"No," Brian replied sadly. "Nobody wants him."

As his father asked God to bless the food, Brian thought of why he felt so close to the dog. *Nobody wants either of us,* he decided. *Please, Lord, find a home for the puppy. Amen,* he added silently to his father's blessing.

They were almost done with supper when they heard the now-familiar scratching at the front door. At his father's nod, Brian bounded to the door and let in the grateful pup.

When Brian noticed that his parents were smiling, he begged once more, "Please let me keep him."

"But Brian, he belongs to someone else," his father insisted.

"Yes, I know," sputtered Brian, "but whoever it is doesn't want him. Why couldn't I—" he fished for the right word "—*adopt* him? Like—you adopted me?"

He had said the hated word, but this time it had sounded different. Before he had kind of spit it out. Now it sounded good, because it had new meaning.

Adopted, adopted, he repeated to himself. *It means someone wants you!* He was so absorbed in his new discovery that he didn't hear his parents' answer.

"You may keep the puppy," his mother repeated twice.

"I'll build him a house in the backyard," his father added.

Brian wasn't sure whether it was getting to keep the puppy or discovering the specialness of being adopted that made him suddenly so happy—and so hungry. "Oh, thank you. Thanks for letting me adopt him," he said, grinning. "And thanks for adopting me—and could I have some dessert now, please?"

"YOU'RE THE NEW SITTER?"

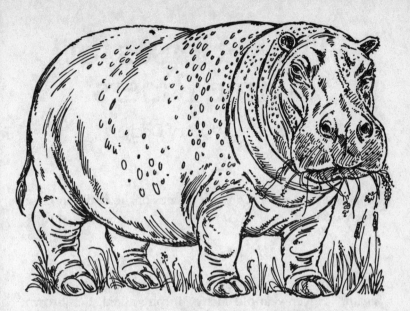

African River Horse

by Gloria A. Truitt

Because he wallows in the mud,
   He's called a *river horse,*
But he's related to the pig,
   And not the horse, of course!
He feeds upon the water plants
   That grow around his home,
And there he stays within his herd
   For he's not known to roam.
Now, if we tried to lift him,
   It would take a lot of us,
For when he's grown, he weighs four tons,
   The hippopotamus!

Three Horses for Three Riders

by Charity Terry Decker

This is a true story. Only the names of the children have been changed.   THE AUTHOR

"Mom, are we really going to live in the country again?" eleven-year-old Misty Murphy asked, her brown eyes dancing with excitement. Misty's nine-year-old sister Melanie and her brother Mike, age six, were helping their mother put cleaning supplies into the car to take to a newly rented house in the desert area east of the Cascade Mountains in Oregon.

"We sure are," her mother answered. "Dad and I are so glad we found that old ranch house. But first we do have to clean it. The previous renters left it in a mess."

"Is there a tree for a swing, Mom?" Melanie asked.

"I think the tree is just the right size for a swing. But we'll see when we get there," Mom answered. "I think we have everything in the car now. All of you get in. Mike, you sit in front with me so I can be sure you wear your seat belt."

Within thirty minutes, they were parking in front of their future home. Everyone climbed out of the car and looked around.

"Oh, Mom!" Mike cried. "Without curtains, the house looks like it wants to cry."

"It does look lonely," Misty said. "But we'll change that, won't we?" She began unloading the mop, broom, and cleaning rags. Since she was the oldest, her mother counted on her help the most. Misty didn't mind. She no longer had to work as hard as she had when they lived on the farm in Alabama.

She still felt like crying whenever she thought of their lovely farm and horse they had left behind. None of them had wanted to sell the farm. But Mom and Dad could not make it support them. Then Dad had found a job with a construction company and they had to move all the way out here to central Oregon and had been renting an apartment in the city for a while.

Oregon was a beautiful state, but Misty missed her grandparents. And she missed the mare, Millie. However, the people who had bought the farm—and Millie—had said they would take good care of her.

"Look, Misty. Look at all the grass!" Melanie called to her. Melanie was standing by the pasture fence, the crisp air fluffing her golden curls.

"May I go see, Mom?" Misty asked as she followed her mother into the house and put down her load.

"We'll both go see," Mom said.

They joined Melanie and Mike beside the fence. It enclosed three acres of the most beautiful grass Misty had seen since coming to Oregon.

"Wouldn't Millie go crazy over this little pasture?" Melanie squealed. "There's a barn over there where we could keep her out of the snow."

"One mare isn't enough for the three of us anymore," Misty said. "Mike can ride now too. What we need are

53

three horses." Misty pulled at her brown hair and wished for a horse for each of them. Of course, she wished hers could be Millie.

"Mom," she said, "why don't you ask Dad if he'll buy each of us a horse? This pasture would be perfect for horses."

Mom looked sad. "I'm sorry, Misty, but Dad and I won't be able to buy horses for a long time. There are too many other things we need. Horses and saddles cost a lot of money. Then in the winter, the grass would die and we would have to buy feed. We can't afford even one horse."

"I want a horse!" Mike wailed. Tears clung to his lashes. Melanie looked as unhappy as Mike. Misty knew they all missed their old way of life.

"Children, perhaps you should talk to God about your desire. He's helped you make new friends here. Perhaps He will help you with the horses."

Misty turned toward the snowcapped mountains— Three Sisters, Mother had called them. They were the major source of water for everyone in the area. God had helped them find this place with water rights. He must have a good reason. It seemed strange—worrying about water. Most of the time it rained plenty in Alabama.

"Well, I guess we must get at that cleaning," Mother reminded them, and they all trooped into the house and spent the next two hours sweeping, dusting, and scrubbing.

That night, back in their apartment, the children prayed that the Lord would send each of them a horse.

By the weekend, they had moved into the ranch house. They all loved their new home and each night at prayertime, the children prayed aloud for three horses. Misty knew God was listening and would answer if it was best for them.

One day at school Misty told her friend Sue Ann about missing Millie. Then she mentioned the clear cool water that came down the irrigation ditch and flooded their pasture, making the grass tall and green.

"We have horses," Sue Ann said. "But we don't have water and grass. Our land has no water rights. We have to keep our horses in a dry, dusty corral. All we have to feed them is dry stuff. I wish we had some of your grass and water."

"I'm so sorry about your animals," Misty said. "I'll ask Mom and Dad if you can put them in our pasture."

When she got home from school Misty told her mother how sorry she felt for her friend's horses. "Couldn't they put them in our pasture?" she asked.

"I don't think so, Misty. We can't be responsible for their animals."

That evening, someone knocked on the door. When Mr. Murphy opened it, there stood Sue Ann and her father. "This is my dad," she said. "I told him about your water and pasture. I hope you don't mind."

Misty's parents introduced themselves and invited their guests in. They listened to what Sue Ann's dad had to say. In a little while, he convinced them to rent their pasture and barn to him.

"What's more, you people may ride any time we aren't using the horses. All three are so gentle that with a little help, even Mike will be able to ride."

After their guests left, Misty, Melanie, and Mike got ready for bed. Then they all knelt to pray as usual. This time it was Melanie's turn to pray first. "Thank You, Father, for everything You've given us, but please help us to get a horse each—"

"Wait!" Mike interrupted. "We do each have a horse! Sue Ann's father said we could ride theirs. There are three horses and three of us!"

The children all looked up at each other and smiled in surprise. It was true. And they had not bought the horses. Neither would they have to provide winter feed for them. Misty was so happy she wanted to sing. Wasn't God wonderful? He had not only answered their prayers, He had answered in the best way for them.

"Thank You, Lord, for giving us three horses to care for," she said, almost laughing aloud for joy.

Princess Tabitha

A FICTION STORY
by Delnora M. Erickson

Cindy Carson woke up early one bright June morning and remembered almost at once: Today is my tenth birthday! She ran to the front door and opened it, thinking she'd run through the wet grass with her bare feet before the sun wiped away the dew. But there on the doorstep sat a big white cat.

The cat looked expectantly at Cindy as if she were waiting to be invited in. So, of course, that's what Cindy did.

"Look, Mother," she called. "My birthday present!"

Mother stepped out of the kitchen and smiled when she saw the cat. "She must belong to someone. A cat that lovely isn't a stray. You can play with her for a while, but don't expect to keep her. She'll soon go home to her owner."

"I'm going to call her Tabitha—Tabby for short. She acts like she's come to stay," Cindy said.

And that's exactly the way Tabitha acted. She walked

calmly around the small living room as if inspecting each chair. When she came to the small rocker, she jumped into it, curled up, and went to sleep.

"Silly kitty," Cindy said with love in her eyes, "you forgot to turn off your motor."

As the days passed, the big white cat showed no sign of leaving even though she was put outside on the doorstep each night. And each morning when Cindy opened the door, Tabitha would be waiting for her breakfast.

Tabitha turned out to be a wise cat. She never jumped onto tables or scratched overstuffed furniture. In fact, she did few of the naughty things cats are fond of doing. While she was partial to certain cat food, she always ate her meals without complaining.

When two weeks had gone by and Tabitha was still there, Cindy's father insisted on putting a notice in the paper about the cat. Still, nothing came of the notice. By

August, Tabitha was a regular part of the family, and no one expected her to leave.

Then one day when Cindy and Tabitha were sitting on the front step and Cindy was reading her favorite book aloud to the cat, a girl stopped on the sidewalk in front of their house. "Princess!" she exclaimed.

In a bound, the cat was down the walk and in the girl's arms. "You naughty cat!" the girl said. "Have you been here all this time?"

Cindy was so shocked, she couldn't think of anything to say. The girl came up the walk, holding Tabitha. "I'm Jenny," she said. "I live quite a way from here, but I'm visiting my grandmother in the next block. I've been looking for Princess for weeks."

By this time, Cindy was feeling very unfriendly toward this stranger who claimed Tabitha with so little ceremony. "B-but she's my cat," Cindy protested. "She came on my birthday and I've had her ever since."

"Princess was given to me when she was a tiny kitten," Jenny said. "We went on a vacation in the middle of June, and I left her with a neighbor. The neighbor said she disappeared the night we left. How long have you had her?"

Cindy did some fast thinking. If she insisted that she had Tabitha since the cat was a kitten, that would cancel Jenny's claim. The cat jumped from Jenny's arms and settled down on the step next to Cindy. There were tears in Cindy's eyes when she finally answered:

"She was here the 16th of June when I opened the door. That was my birthday—but I guess she is yours." With that Cindy put her head in her arms and sobbed.

Jenny hesitated a moment, then gathered the cat into her arms again. "I'm sorry. I know you love her, but I love her too." She got up and walked down the sidewalk, then stopped as if thinking and came back to Cindy. "If you wanted her so much, why did you tell me when you got her?" she asked.

Cindy lifted a tear-streaked face. "Well, I love Jesus," she said slowly. "I know He wouldn't want me to lie just to keep Tabitha."

Jenny just looked at her a long minute then said, "Tell you what; we're going to be moving in about a month. We're going far away and will be living in an apartment. Mother said I would have to get another home for Princess. I've missed her so much that I've been hoping that if I found her, Mother would let me take her with us. I know you've been good to her or she wouldn't have stayed with you. Before we move, I'll bring her back, OK?"

Cindy nodded and smiled.

Jenny turned around at the end of their walk and called back, "Let's call her Princess Tabitha. Then she'll know she belongs to us both."

"Thanks," Cindy called as she waved good-bye.

It seemed like a long month. Every day she opened the door in the morning, hoping that by chance Tabitha had come back. But there was no sign of her. She wondered too if Jenny would keep her word.

Then one day the doorbell rang. When Cindy opened the door, sure enough, there stood Jenny with the cat in her arms. Princess Tabitha jumped down and headed for the living room and her favorite chair. She jumped into it, curled into a ball, and began to purr. The girls looked at each other and laughed.

"May I come in?" Jenny asked. "Mother said I could stay a few minutes. We're moving tomorrow."

"Of course," Cindy said. "Come in. I'm so excited about having Princess Tabitha again I forgot to be polite." The girls sat together on the couch. Something seemed to be bothering Jenny. She started to speak several times. Finally she said, "When I was here before, you said you loved Jesus.

"I go to Sunday School and believe in God. I know Jesus died for our sins, but I don't know if I really love Him. And I don't think I'd tell the truth like you did if I thought I'd lose Princess."

Cindy smiled. "Two years ago, I prayed and asked the Lord Jesus to forgive my sins and take charge of my life. I know He came into my heart to live there."

Jenny looked wistful. "I'd sure like to know He lives in me," she said.

"Oh, you can," Cindy cried. "I'll get my Bible." She hurried to her room and turned to one of her favorite Bible verses. Returning, she showed the verse to Jenny. "Read it," she said.

" 'Behold, I stand at the door, and knock; if any man hear My voice, and open the door, I will come in to him, and will sup with him, and he with Me' " (Revelation 3:20, KJV), Jenny read aloud.

"You see, He wants to come and live in you," Cindy explained. "You just have to ask Him to make you clean and take charge of your life."

Jenny nodded, tears shining in her eyes. "Now I understand. Will you pray with me?"

While Princess Tabitha purred happily in her chair, the girls bowed their heads and Jenny asked Jesus to forgive all her sin and come and live in her. Then Cindy thanked Jesus for bringing Jenny to her and for Tabitha who helped bring them together.

His Donkey Knew Best

by Eva Doerksen

GIN, A NIGERIAN CHRISTIAN YOUTH, LEADS A LOADED DONKEY TO MARKET. IT'S GETTING LATE. AND HE SEES A VILLAGE AHEAD...

MAYBE I CAN FIND A PLACE TO STAY THERE.

MAY I HAVE A PLACE TO SLEEP IN YOUR COMPOUND?

OUR HOUSES ARE FULL. GO TO THE NEXT VILLAGE. IT ISN'T FAR.

THEY MUST THINK I'M A THIEF. I DON'T KNOW HOW FAR THE NEXT VILLAGE REALLY IS SO WE'D BETTER STAY IN THIS FIELD.

by Van Seenen

TAKEN BY EVA DOERKSEN, WITH PERMISSION, FROM BLACK GEMS FOR HIS CROWN, SUDAN INTERIOR MISSION, © 1951

His Donkey Knew Best

Chu Chu

A TRUE STORY
told by Nathan Diehl
written by Jeri McCoy

Chu Chu is a cute little dog, about eighteen inches high. She has a lot of hair over one eye, front legs that always need brushing, and the shaggy mitten-paws of a Lhasa Apso. She's black and white with patches of brown on each ear—which, by the way, she perks up at the slightest sound while wagging her feathery tail. And she's smart!

The first day at home, Chu Chu learned "shake hands" and "sit up pretty." (She knows she's pretty and even likes to look at herself in the pool.)

She learns fast. I was brushing her when Dad returned from work one day. Chu Chu ran to greet him. "You get back there and lie down to be brushed," he told her. We couldn't believe it when she immediately plopped herself down in front of me with all four paws straight up.

By the next week Chu Ch learned to "sit" and "roll over." After that she easily learned "fetch your brush," and "put it back." To test her understanding of our words,

I ordered her to "go to bed." She went off—slowly—and laid down on her bed.

One day when Chu Chu and I returned home from a walk, I dropped her leash so she could run down the long driveway. She stopped, picked the leash up, and brought it back to me, her eyes saying, "You dropped my leash."

Anyway, we had fallen in love with her before we discovered that she's really different. I mean weird. Believe it or not, she acts as if she's part cat. And for all we know, she may have been raised by one. You see, we know nothing about her parents because we found her at the county dog pound.

We were sure she was too small to get out of our fenced yard. Wrong! One day when I got home from school, she was gone. I panicked, then called her name just once.

She got there so fast I couldn't tell where she came from. It was as if she had fallen from the sky. I was happy

65

enough to cry. We checked the fence for holes, but couldn't find any.

The next day our neighbor told us that she had seen Chu Chu leap to the top of our fence, then walk around it as easily as a cat. Chu Chu visited all the neighbors on their patios. A jogger even stopped to watch her walking on the fence. "Whew!" he said. "I thought I had jogged too long."

And you won't believe this, but the sound she makes when she wants to go out is something between a whine and a meow, but closer to a "m-e-o-w." Furthermore, when she's getting a lot of petting, which she lives for, she purrs. And what do you think her favorite treats are? Yep—fish, milk, and ice cream. Maybe she *is* part cat.

One time when Chu Chu was *meowing* to ride with my dad in his van, he told her to jump in. Suddenly, as Dad was driving along at about 25 miles per hour, Chu Chu leaped out of the window into oncoming traffic! Dodging and darting between cars, she ran into a nearby shopping center. Quickly Dad pulled into the shopping center and gave chase. When he got home, he was angry and embarrassed.

"Couldn't we please name her something else?" he begged Mom. "People in the shopping center looked at me as if I were crazy, running around calling, 'CHU CHU!'"

So you see, Chu Chu even seems to have nine lives like a cat.

Once, after jumping up on the fence, I told her, "Chu Chu, you are a dog, a California canine. You are not a cat. There is no way you should be able—like Superman—to reach the top of that fence in a single bound."

With her eyes, she told me, "You just don't understand,

do you?"

Since she is so smart and usually obeys so fast, we know that when she doesn't obey and runs out of the yard, she is openly defying us. While visiting our neighbor, she learned that their terrier has a doggy door. She must have thought, *How neat! That lucky dog can go in and out whenever he wants.* Sure enough, the next night our neighbor got home and found Chu Chu in his house, playing with his dog.

Our kind neighbor was sympathetic. "I don't know how you're going to keep her inside your yard," he said. "She thinks she is a cat. She has coil springs for legs."

We tried all kinds of things to keep her in the yard. We fastened the gate that she had clawed up, just as a cat would. We even put a slippery strip of paneling across the top of the gate so she couldn't get a clawhold. And, much to my delight, my parents accepted a puppy from a friend. They thought that if Chu Chu had company during the day when they were at work and I was at school, she would stay home.

But the first day we had the puppy, our neighbor greeted us with, "You aren't going to believe this, but—" With very little effort, Chu Chu had jumped to the top of the fence again. She pulled the copper tubing out of the latch with her mouth and opened the gate. Then she took the puppy with her on her morning walk. He strutted along beside her, looking at her with admiration.

Chu Chu is a California dog. She would not like snowy weather because, like a cat, she hates to put her paws on wet ground. Sometimes during our rainy season, she refuses to go outside for several hours. So Dad fixed up a dry, running path outdoors for her.

We've finally decided that Chu Chu is not sure she's a

67

dog. And maybe she *was* raised by a cat. She certainly *thinks* she's a cat. In fact, Mom says that Chu Chu is "a living example of the power of positive thinking." Because she thinks she's a cat, she can do what cats do. But most important, we love her just the way she is.

The Flying Squirrel

A NATURE STORY
by Grace Fox Anderson

Like the man "on the flying trapeze," the flying squirrel glides through the air "with the greatest of ease." His gliding is made possible by a thin, soft fold of skin that stretches from his forefeet to his back feet. When he spreads out his legs, the skin stretches out like a square kite and enables him to travel as far as 150 feet at a time!

This little acrobat doesn't take chances, however. He looks from side to side before he leaps—to make sure he is high enough above trees and buildings. Then he leaps and glides, using his flat, featherlike tail as a rudder. As soon as he lands, he runs quickly around the tree he's landed on to make sure no enemy is around.

If you were to see him on the ground, you could recognize him because the extra skin makes him look as if he's wearing oversized clothes! Unfortunately, you may never see a flying squirrel since he is active only at night and sleeps during the day.

His fur is soft and pretty, ranging from grayish buff to

dark gray. He is all white underneath and has bright, intelligent eyes. He may be anywhere from eight and one-half to ten inches long, including his tail.

These furry gliders usually live high off the ground in forests of beech or maple trees. They often make their nests in abandoned woodpecker holes, unused gray-squirrel nests, empty birdhouses, or even in abandoned houses.

In the winter, several "flyers" may hole up together to keep warm. But in the spring and summer, the nest is usually occupied only by one mother and her two to four young.

Flying squirrels are very curious. Because of this they sometimes get into big trouble. They like to examine traps set for other animals and often get caught themselves.

They feed mainly on nuts such as pecans, walnuts, peanuts, chestnuts, and acorns. What they don't eat, they store for future use. In the winter or early spring, they also eat the buds of some trees. And in the summer, they eat berries and leaves.

They make good pets too. (But one must always be careful when handling a wild squirrel because it can carry rabies.) At first, when captured, the flying squirrel is very quiet. But when the owner has shown by kind actions and good food that he is the squirrel's friend, the little fellow will chatter away. He even makes funny noises in his throat that sound like laughter when something pleases him.

What a delightful creature God has given us to enjoy in this furry little acrobat!

The Live Christmas Tree Ornament

by Mary Emma Allen

This is a true story, based on the author's own experience with a real pet squirrel. THE EDITOR

Katy heard Frisker's excited barking out in the yard and ran to the window. Outside she saw the dog chasing a tiny, gray squirrel that was too small even to climb back up the old oak tree.

"Stop, Frisker!" she cried, running outdoors. "You can't have that baby squirrel."

Katy picked up the tiny squirrel.* It was soft and furry with a long, fluffy tail. The baby squirrel was frightened, and trembled in her hands.

"Now, Chippy Squirrel," Katy said, "don't be afraid. I'm not going to hurt you."

She took Chippy into the house and fed him warm milk

---

*Wild squirrels can carry deadly rabies, so it is not wise to pick them up. If you must, wear heavy gloves. Moreover, today some states have laws against keeping wild animals as pets, but not when Katy was a girl.

from a doll bottle. Then she made a warm bed for him in a box lined with soft flannel.

To keep him warm at night Katy put a hot-water bottle under the flannel. Then she placed the box beside her bed.

One morning, when Katy reached inside the box, Chippy felt cold and didn't move. The hot-water bottle had cooled, and Chippy had become chilled. Katy thought he was dead, but then she saw him breathing just a tiny bit.

She rushed downstairs where Mother was cooking breakfast on the woodburning cookstove. "O Mama!" she cried. "Chippy got too cold last night. May I hold him near the oven for a few minutes to get him warm?"

"Yes, Katy, but be careful," Mother answered.

Katy held Chippy in her hands and rubbed his fur so the warm air could get close to his skin. Slowly, very slowly, he began to stretch his legs and move his head.

Before the day was over, he was scampering around once again and hiding in all his favorite places around the house.

Nuts became Chippy's favorite food. He hid them all over the house. Katy never knew when she'd step on one under a rug or find one in a coat pocket. One night when she crawled into bed, she discovered that Chippy had tucked a hard nut under her sheet!

As Chippy grew older, he slept in a box in the basement. When he wanted to come upstairs, he'd scratch on the basement door until someone heard him and let him inside.

When Christmastime came, Chippy had great fun. He scampered through the ornaments as Katy and her two brothers and sister decorated the Christmas tree. One day

The Live Christmas Tree Ornament

Katy found him sitting on a branch, nibbling a nut. After that, he enjoyed romping about the branches. He'd walk way out on a branch until it bent beneath his weight. Then when he slipped, he'd end up looking just like a wiggly, furry ornament, dangling from the tree.

"He's our live Christmas tree ornament," Katy said, laughing.

Chippy soon learned to stay away from the lights. They were too hot for his little paws. But the family noticed that popcorn and cookie decorations began to disappear and candy canes grew shorter. Yes, Chippy had found he could have a long, delightful feast from the tree.

Then a couple of days before Christmas, Chippy disappeared. He didn't come around to eat or play on the Christmas tree. Katy called and called, "Chippy, here Chippy! Time to eat!"

But Chippy didn't appear. Then Katy discovered that the basement door to the outside had been left open a crack. "Oh, no!' she exclaimed. "He must have gone out that way. I'm afraid Frisker has caught him."

When Daddy came home that night, he said, "I just saw a squirrel scampering along the porch roof. I think it was Chippy."

Katy rushed out and saw Chippy jump from the porch roof to the tree beside the house. "Here, Chippy," she called. "I'll take you back inside."

But Chippy just climbed higher in the tree, so Katy couldn't reach him.

"He won't come to me," Katy said when she went inside. "He just scampers away."

"Katy," Mother said, "you must remember that Chippy is a wild creature. God made him to live outside. He wants to live there where he can be with other squirrels."

"But it's so lonesome without him," Katy answered.

Finally the night before Christmas arrived. The whole family missed their frisky little friend, playing in the Christmas tree as they gathered around it at bedtime. Katy and her older brother and sister sat at Mother's feet, while her baby brother sat on Mother's lap. Daddy relaxed in his easy chair and read the Christmas story from the Bible as he did each year.

While he was reading about Jesus' birth, Katy heard chattering coming from the Christmas tree.

"Oh, look!" one of Katy's brothers cried. "Someone must have left the basement door open again."

There was Chippy, perched at the very top of the tree. "He thinks he's the Christmas star," Katy said, laughing.

The whole family was glad to see Chippy again. As Daddy finished reading the account of Jesus coming to earth, Katy sighed contentedly. It looked as if her live ornament had come to stay with them a little while longer before going to live outdoors for good.

Surprise in the Woods

A FICTION STORY
by Sara Ann DuBose

Kathy was excited. There was nothing in the world she enjoyed more than exploring. It was a perfect spring Saturday and Dad had just asked if she would like to go riding with him on the old Milton Road, a country road near their home.

"You bet!" Kathy shouted. "Just give me five minutes to put on my jeans."

After helping Dad pump air into their bike tires, Kathy raced him down their winding street. "Hurry," she called back to him. "Maybe we can get away before Fluffy follows us."

They rode single file as they pulled out onto a busy street, then turned off into the thick woods along Milton Road. Kathy knew it was going to be a perfect day.

Honeysuckle and other fresh green smells filled the air. Kathy decided spring was her favorite time of the year. She knew by the smile on Dad's face that he was enjoying it too.

After a sharp bend in the unpaved road, it divided in two. Kathy chose the most interesting fork, urging Dad to follow.

This path was narrow—too narrow for a car, but fine for bikes. As they slowed to ride around a fallen tree, Kathy heard a funny noise behind the large stump. She stopped pedaling.

"Wait, Dad. Shhh. There's something behind that stump. Do you hear it?"

Dad leaned his bike against a tree and walked over to see. Kathy followed him. "It looks like a couple of puppies," he said.

"Oh, Daddy, I wonder how they got here?" Kathy said as she stooped and reached out to one puffy brown ball with ears and tail.

"It does seem strange that they'd be out here so far from anything," her father said. "Maybe the mother dog is nearby."

"I hope so," Kathy said. "They're so small, but their eyes are open."

"They must be no more than five or six weeks old," her father said. "Surely the mother dog must be around somewhere." He walked around in the woods, looking while Kathy stayed by the puppies.

"Can I pick up this brown one?" she asked.

"I guess so, but they might have fleas."

Kathy wasn't worried about fleas. But she was worried about the two tiny puppies alone in the woods with nothing to eat. "Aren't they cute, Daddy?"

"Yes," Dad answered. He stooped down and picked up the white one. "But I think we'd better leave them for now," he said. "They look too healthy to have been abandoned—unless something has happened to their mother.

78

Tell you what. We'll come back tomorrow and see if the mother comes around. OK?"

"I guess so," Kathy said. "But I hate to think of leaving them alone. Can we take them home tomorrow if the mother dog doesn't show up?"

"We'll see," Dad said.

Kathy hated riding off and leaving the puppies. It did seem strange that a mother dog would give birth so far from any homes. Kathy was afraid that someone had left them there to die. She didn't sleep well that night, thinking about them. On the way to Sunday School the next day Daddy said they would check on the puppies that afternoon after dinner.

"Are you ready to go, Kathy?" Daddy called after they'd eaten. "We'd better drive this time, just in case."

"And I'll take some scraps of meat along," Kathy said, grinning. "Bye, Mom. I enjoyed dinner."

As they drove along, Kathy prayed that the puppies would still be there and all right.

"This is as far as we can go in the car, Kathy," her father said when they came to the fork in the road. "We'll have to walk the rest of the way. Bring your scraps with you."

They hurried along the path until they came to the stump. Kathy was almost afraid to look. "Puppies, are you there?" she called, peering over the top. She saw the same two balls of fur looking up as if they have been waiting for her.

"I brought you something," she said, holding out her hand. But they only sniffed as if they didn't know what to do with the meat.

"They're probably too young for solid food," Daddy said, taking the scraps from her and rubbing a piece of ham on the brown puppy's nose.

He reached out a small pink tongue and licked at the meat.

Not to be left out, the white puppy brushed up against the brown one and took a bite, just missing Dad's finger.

"Oh, Daddy, they're so hungry. We've got to take them home. They don't even have water here."

Dad scratched his head in thought. "We'd better take them back for tonight. But tomorrow we'll call the animal shelter. We have Fluffy. We can't have any more dogs. The shelter should be able to find a good home for two puppies."

"But what if they can't?" Kathy wailed.

"Kathy, we can't take them in. But I'm sure a lot of people want puppies. Let's take them now, OK?"

Kathy held both puppies in her lap while Daddy drove. Already she was thanking the Lord for taking care of them and planning what she'd put them in when they got home.

Everyone got into the act at home. Even Kathy's older sister who usually was talking on the phone came out to admire the puppies. Mother brought them some warm milk, then sat for a while in the grass with the girls and played with the puppies. By late afternoon, Kathy had given each dog a name and was planning a special bed for them on the back porch.

Later, when Daddy came out, Kathy held Tender, the brown puppy, up to him and said, "He likes it here, Daddy. Couldn't we just keep this one?"

"I'm sorry, Kathy, but we can't afford another dog."

Kathy drew Tender back to her face and tried not to cry. Somehow, it was almost a relief when Mother called them to come and eat. During the blessing, Kathy prayed about the puppies again and by the time she was helping clear the table, she had an idea.

"Mom, could you wait until after I get home from school tomorrow to call the animal shelter? Maybe my friend Shannon knows someone who would like a puppy. We could even go through the neighborhood and ask."

"I suppose so, Kathy."

After school the next day, Kathy and Shannon walked through the neighborhood with the puppies in a box. An hour later they were back with one puppy left—Tender. "Mission halfway accomplished," Kathy told her parents when they got home. "Mrs. Hopkins had a fit over Snowball. She said she and Mr. Hopkins might keep him or give him to a niece. Isn't that great? Now we only have to worry about Tender."

"Kathy, I must call the animal shelter. Do you understand?" Mom asked.

"Yes, Mother, I understand," Kathy answered.

Her mother made the phone call, then told Kathy that the truck from the animal shelter wouldn't be there till the next day. Kathy breathed a sigh of relief and got out an old rag. She let Tender tug on it till Mother told her to get busy on her homework.

The next day Kathy expected to come home and find Tender's box empty, but her mother told her the people hadn't come yet for the puppy. Kathy leaned over his box and picked him up. "How can I give you up?" she murmured in his soft brown ear.

Just then she saw a truck coming toward the house. She picked up Tender and walked out to meet the truck. "I'm going to be brave," she told Tender.

"Did you come for the puppy?" Kathy called out to the driver.

"What puppy?" he asked.

"This one." Kathy held Tender up high.

"No. I'm with the Park and Recreation Department for the city. I was just turning around in your driveway until I saw you walking out this way. Do you have a puppy for sale?"

"Not for sale. I'll give him away to anyone who will give him a good home."

"Hmmm. May I see him?"

Kathy handed Tender to the man through the truck window. She noticed he took him carefully and smiled.

"My son has been wanting a puppy. This would be quite a surprise for Jeff. Could I really have him?"

"Yes, sir," Kathy said, smiling. "But please take him to a vet for his shots and everything. We found him in the woods, and you want to be sure he's OK. His name is Tender."

"Fine. I'll take good care of him. And thank you. Jeff will be so happy."

Kathy waved and turned back toward her house, thinking: *Mom can call the animal shelter and cancel their trip. How wonderful that they were late!* Kathy felt happy and sad all at the same time. She knew she would miss Tender and Snowball, but deep down inside she knew God never promised to give her everything she wanted. At least both puppies had a good home.

She looked up at the porch and saw Fluffy waiting and wagging his tail. Poor Fluffy had been ignored for two days. Kathy ran up the steps and threw her arms around him.

King of the Skies

A NATURE STORY
by Ken Anderson

One summer morning I stood on a lakeshore in northern Michigan. Suddenly, I noticed something flying overhead. I looked up and there, high above me, glided a bald eagle.

I had seen eagles before, but never one flying that close. I realized then that the bird is every inch a king. No wonder the Congress of the United States, back in 1782, chose the bald eagle as America's emblem of power.

Quite an interesting story is told about that choice. Benjamin Franklin, it seems, wanted to make the turkey gobbler the national bird. He said the eagle is a coward and bully and thief.

It is true that the golden eagle sometimes steals lambs and chickens, even small calves from cattle herds. But not the bald eagle! His favorite food is fish. In fact, that's about all he eats. He always minds his own business. And, if left alone, he harms no one.

Stories of eagles stealing human babies, for instance,

are not true. The American Audubon Society, specializing in protecting animals and birds, has carefully checked these stories and found them untrue.

The eagle's nest is an amazing structure. Other birds build a new nest each year. They move from tree to tree and may even go many miles to build a new home.

Not so with eagles.

Each year the eagle builds a new nest on top of the old one. Since an eagle may live sixty to seventy years, his nest grows and grows. It is his permanent home all year.

Once an eagle's nest was found which weighed nearly two tons. That's 4,000 pounds! It was at least 100 years old. Nests have been found with enough sticks and leaves to fill several small trucks.

To look at an eagle's egg, you wouldn't think he would be much of a bird. The egg is less than three inches long—only half the size of a whistling swan's egg.

Since the eagle is not hatched as a very large bird, it takes him a long time to grow up. But because he grows slowly, his body has time to get strong.

From the beginning, his parents teach him things he needs to know. The eaglet learns to grasp sticks with his talons. He must also learn how to tear up a fish so he can eat it. Of course, the most important thing an eaglet learns is how to fly.

The little bird can't just step out the back door. His home may be on the top of some mountain or at the top of a towering tree. So he must jump out at the risk of his life.

His parents help him. They hold bits of food a short distance away from the nest. He reaches out, but it is too far for him to grasp. The only way he can get at it is to jump.

At last he jumps into thin air! Now he must fly or fall.

Often the young eagle is not strong enough to fly. But his parents seem to understand. If he falls, screaming for help, either parent will swoop down and catch him before he hits the ground. Then he is brought back to the nest where he may be left for several weeks until his wings grow stronger. Then he must try to fly again.

Once the eagle has learned to fly, he spends less and less time around his parents' nest, for eagles love to fly. When fully developed, the young bird will find his own place in the world.

The adult eagle has a wingspread of as much as eight feet. His feathers may be twenty inches long. And he has great strength in his flight feathers or pinions.

The eagle's wing tips are slotted. That means he can spread these feathers apart like fingers. Because he can do this, he is able to soar without flapping his wings.

And the eagle always seems to be soaring. He hardly ever flaps his wings. No wonder Solomon wrote: "There be . . . things which are too wonderful for me . . . the way of an eagle in the air!" (Proverbs 30:18-19, KJV)

Another interesting thing about the eagle is his eyesight. God has given this bird eyes like miniature telescopes so the great creature can find his food even though he flies high in the sky. He has been known to see a fish three miles down. With one long dive he can catch that same fish!

It isn't strange that Isaiah should point us to the soaring king of the skies and say, "They that wait upon the Lord shall renew their strength; they shall mount up with wings as eagles; they shall run, and not be weary; and they shall walk, and not faint" (Isaiah 40:31, KJV).

Pablo and Burrito

A TRUE STORY
by Esther L. Vogt

Pablo lived in a small village in Mexico. It was his job each morning to water his family's few cows and El Burrito (Little Burro). Afterward, Pablo would take the cows to pasture outside the village. Then he was free until evening.

The eleven-year-old boy and the little brown burro were good friends. They spent hours together on the village streets.

One day as Pablo rode Burrito down the hot, dusty street, the boy laid his face against the animal's soft neck. "My stomach feels like an empty cave," he told Burrito. "We never have enough food at home. Where can I find something for us to eat?"

As the donkey clopped along, Pablo smelled the fragrance of fresh rolls drifting from the bakery. The boy sniffed hungrily. *That's it!* he said to himself. *The bakers are usually busy in the back of the shop. They come to the counter only when they hear the front door open. I'll sneak in and—just hope I'm lucky!*

He slid from Burrito's back and quietly opened the bakery door. No one came. A basketful of fragrant sweet rolls sat near the door. Pablo snatched two for Burrito and stuffed them into his pockets. He grabbed another for himself.

As Pablo dashed out, he heard footsteps. He sprang on the burro's back and Burrito clattered away. But before Burrito had trotted around the corner, Martin, the baker's teenage son, yelled at him. "What did you want, Pablo? Why didn't you ask? We—"

But Pablo and Burrito trotted away in a cloud of dust, paying no attention to Martin. Some donkeys were lazy, but Burrito could really travel when he wanted to.

Pablo and the burro headed for the creek at the edge of town. There, on the grassy bank, they enjoyed their rolls. Burrito didn't seem to mind that his were squashed.

Later, Pablo led Burrito into the corral, then went for the cows. When he got home, his mother was standing in the doorway of their house with her hands on her hips. "Pablo, bring those cows in and come here pronto!" she ordered.

Pablo could tell by her "you'd-better-mind-or-else" tone that there was trouble. Dragging his feet, he returned to the house. There stood husky Martin, looking very serious.

Pablo cringed and waited for the spanking he knew must follow. *The way Martin stares at me,* Pablo thought, *you'd think I'd run off with the whole basketful of rolls instead of three small ones."*

"Do you know why I've come?" Martin asked. Amazingly, his voice sounded kind.

Pablo fidgeted. "I think I do. But I've already eaten

them, so what can you do?" he jeered.

"What?" his mother screeched. "You mean, Pablo, that it's true you stole those rolls? You're a bad boy. How many times have I told you not to steal?"

She whirled around to Martin. "We've spanked him and sent him to confession, but still he makes trouble in the village!"

Martin raised his hand. "Just a minute, Señora. I want to ask him a question.

"Pablo, do you know why you took those rolls?"

Pablo nodded. "Because Burrito and I were hungry. We hadn't eaten since breakfast and our stomachs were as empty as the caves in the hills!"

Martin turned to Mama. "If we could teach your son to ask for things honestly, he wouldn't have to steal. Spankings and confessing to the priest won't change him, you know. But I know Someone who can."

"How much will it cost?" Mama asked anxiously. "We don't have much money."

"I used to be bad myself, Señora," Martin said quietly. "And Someone changed me. May my parents and I come back tonight when your husband is home? We will tell you about my experience."

"Yes. Why not? Come after supper."

Martin left, and Pablo sighed with relief. Martin hadn't seemed angry. But maybe when he came back tonight he'd beat him.

At the supper table, Papa took another tortilla and scooped up some beans. "Anything happen today, Mama?"

Pablo hunched down into his chair as Mama told him about Pablo's trouble and Martin's visit.

Papa's face turned purple. "Martin is coming back tonight? Why are you such a bad boy, Pablo?"

"You wouldn't believe it," Mama said, "but Martin didn't seem angry. He asked a few questions and said he would come back tonight. He will tell us who can change Pablo."

"Change Pablo?" Papa flared. "Who can change this disobedient boy? But as long as Martin doesn't make trouble, he's welcome!"

When Martin and his parents came, they seemed friendly and glad for a chance to talk. "I understand Pablo took the rolls because he was hungry," Martin said. "Try asking first next time, Pablo, and see what happens. But I believe there's another reason why Pablo makes trouble in the village."

Papa perked up. "What's that?"

"Sin," answered Martin.

Sin? Pablo had heard people confess their sins at church. *But their sins must have been bigger than simply snatching a few rolls!* he decided.

Martin began to read out of a little Book that he called God's Word. " 'For all have sinned, and come short of the glory of God' [Romans 3:23]. Pablo, that's you too. Jesus, God's Son, wants to take away your sin and make you a different boy—a new boy."

Papa nodded. "Very good. Make Pablo do everything he should do to be good."

"No, Señor," said the baker, "only those who want Jesus to be the Ruler in their own lives can be changed. You must let Jesus work in *you,* just as the señora and Pablo and the rest of us must let Jesus clean us up."

Before Martin and his parents left, they handed Pablo a little Book and a brown paper bag full of sweet rolls. At bedtime, Pablo and his family ate the rolls. Pablo read a few verses to his parents from the little Book.

In the days that followed, Pablo and Burrito stopped for free rolls at the bakery whenever they were hungry. Every evening, Pablo read aloud two chapters of the little Book (the Gospel of John). The family enjoyed the stories of Jesus. He seemed like a kind Man—like Martin—only better!

Pablo began to want to be like this wonderful Jesus. Papa and Mama received Jesus as their Saviour, and after that, they changed. Pablo noticed that they prayed to Jesus now.

One day when Pablo went to the bakery for his rolls, he decided to talk to Martin. "Martin, I am ready to give my life to Jesus," he said simply. And right there Pablo asked Jesus to forgive and change him—to make him a new boy.

Pablo no longer steals. Instead, he tries to do what pleases God.

Masked Fisherman

by Gloria A. Truitt

Folks always laugh and say I wear
   A mask across my eyes,
But, honestly, it's just my face,
   And not a strange disguise!
I travel with my family
   To catch my food at night,
And people who have seen me say,
   "It's quite a charming sight."
I fish beside a woodland brook
   That shines beneath the moon,
Then rinse my catch before I eat,
   For I am a raccoon!

How to Love a Hamster

A TRUE STORY
by Barbara Jean Fewell

Did you know that hamsters and people have something special in common? Yes—they both need love in order to live.

I've raised three sons and have eight grandchildren, so I thought I knew all about love. But one day my oldest grandchild, twelve-year-old David, told me that I might know about loving people, but I didn't know the first thing about loving a hamster.

Of course, owning a hamster wasn't my idea in the first place. It all started with my boss at work. One day she whizzed past my desk all excited about something. "Hey, Barb," she said, "we girls here at the office have decided to do something about your loneliness."

"Oh, what's that?" I asked, trying not to sound suspicious.

"We think that after living alone for so long, you need a pet."

Right away I decided that bosses weren't very smart.

Didn't she know that the mobile park where I lived wouldn't allow me to have an animal?

I was just about to remind her of this when she asked, "Will they let you have a pet in a cage?"

"Well, I guess so," I replied, starting to get worried, "but I can't stand birds. They're too messy."

"How about a hamster?"

"A hamster!" I gasped. "No way!"

But my boss kept after me. "Wait a minute, Barb. Since your family lives so far away, you've got to have something to love. My teenage boys raise hamsters and can tell you all about them. In fact, we have just the one for you. It's a male, and entirely different from any hamster you may have seen. I'll bring him in tomorrow, and if you don't like him, we'll forget it. OK?"

Well, what else could I say but yes? She was my boss, wasn't she?

As it turned out the little fellow was all she said and more. He really wasn't like other hamsters. He had personality! His coat was honey-colored with a white fur collar around his neck.

Have you ever looked at a horse or dog and known it was a purebred? That's the way it was with this hamster. I could tell he had breeding! After the first look, I knew we'd be buddies for life.

The first night I had the little fellow, I laid awake trying to think up a good name for him. Then I remembered that because hamsters are rodents, they're related to squirrels and woodchucks. That was it! I'd call him Chuck, short for "woodchuck."

I had been alone for so long that at first it was hard to have another creature around. But Chuck was as happy as he could be. He'd peer out of his cage at me with his big black eyes. His pink paws looked almost like human hands. I couldn't help but like him.

However, it wasn't long before I realized we had problems. You see, at first we were too busy getting to know each other to worry about a proper house or food for Chuck. My boss let me use her cage for a few days.

"Oh, dear," I said to Chuck one morning, "we've got to get you a bigger house, but I can't afford a hamster cage right now."

Little did I know a big surprise was waiting for Chuck and me down at the office. The women at work had found out about my lack of money and gave me a hamster party!

Here's a list of gifts Chuck received—in case you ever own a little "Chuck" of your own:

1. A hamster cage with tubes that the pet can run through.
2. A private room for the top of the cage. (This is where the hamster will build a nest.)
3. A small cage to attach to the main one. I call it Chuck's sun room.
4. A disk to spin on in the sun room.
5. Plenty of hamster food.
6. A hamster wheel.
7. A water container. (Hamsters drink gallons!)
8. Sunflower seeds and small nuts for treats.

Chuck finally had all he needed. At least, that's what I thought. After all, I fed and watered him every day and kept his cage clean.

But it wasn't long before Chuck stopped spinning around on his wheel at night. (Hamsters are night creatures, you know.) He even began to look sick and sad. And soon he wasn't eating right either. And this grandma was worried!

How to Love a Hamster

Just in time, my grandson David came to visit me during his summer vacation. He was eager to see Chuck and brought him a ball to spin around in. But when David looked in at Chuck, he was shocked. "Grandma, what's the matter with him?" he cried.

"I don't know," I said. "He has good food and a nice home, but he's going to die if he gets much worse."

"I hope you're loving him," David said, picking Chuck up and stroking his fur.

After a while he held the little fellow out to me. "Here, Grandma—you hold him."

I must have jumped three feet in the air. "Are you kidding? Don't ask me to handle a hamster. It would be like petting a rat!"

"Grandma! Chuck is one of God's creatures. If you don't pet him once in a while, he'll die. Like people, he needs love!"

It took a few minutes for David's words to sink in. Finally, I got up the courage to put Chuck on my shoulder. He nestled close to me and seemed to love every stroke I gave him.

Things are great between Chuck and me now that I've learned what loving a hamster is all about. I just shudder to think what would have happened to my little friend if David hadn't come for a visit.

Wolves on the Trail

A TRUE STORY
by Jennie Johnson

Father knocked on my bedroom door before sunrise. With a groan, I opened one eye and looked at the clock on the dresser. It was 4:30, the time he had promised to wake me.

Quickly throwing on some warm clothes and grabbing a wool jacket, I headed for the kitchen. Father had turned on only a small light in order not to wake up my mother and younger sister who were still sleeping.

We filled a thermos bottle with hot cocoa and stuffed our pockets with packages of trail mix. Then Father took a rifle and a box of bullets from the gun cabinet. Sometimes I carried a .22 rifle too when we went animal hunting. Today we would be looking for wolves. But only *looking!* The gun was just for our protection.

In a few minutes we were bouncing along in our old green jeep, heading for the scrubby hills about ten miles west of Tucson, Arizona. Ranchers in the area had recently reported seeing several gray wolves roaming around their pastures and corrals.

Wolves are not usually found in Arizona, but there had been a shortage of rain in Mexico the previous year. The desperate animals had come north for food and water. Mexican gray wolves tend to be shy of people, but won't hesitate to kill sheep or chicken. If the wolf pack that moved north was strong enough and very hungry, it might attack a cow or a horse out in open pasture. So the ranchers in the area had been keeping their livestock penned up until the wolves returned to Mexico.

It was still dark out and the early morning air was chilly, but I shivered more with excitement than from cold.

"I sure hope we get to see some wolves today," Father said, smiling. "Last week I was out this way and spotted three different wolf packs in the desert."

I grinned back. "People would think we're crazy if they knew how much we enjoy coming out here just to watch animals."

"I'd rather look at them than kill them," Father agreed. The thought of harming God's creatures unnecessarily seemed cruel and unfair to us.

A pink glow filled the eastern sky as Father turned onto a dirt road in the middle of nowhere. The jeep bounced along for several miles until we came to a flat spot and Father parked.

He led me along an almost invisible game trail, down a steep hillside. In the dim light I could make out a tiny, slant-roof lean-to. Father had built it the week before by laying ocotillo and saguaro cactus sticks over a branch frame.

We stooped and entered the four-foot square room. It had rickety walls and a gap about a foot wide for a doorway. The shack offered little shelter from wind or cold. Father had built it as a "blind," a place in which a hunter or animal watcher could hide and peer out through the walls at whatever came down the trail.

Father pulled out a slim wolf caller made of wood and blew hard on it. Then he cupped one hand over the other end and alternately opened and closed it to make the shrill sounds of a wounded rabbit.

We sat still for several minutes, but all was quiet. Father blew on the wolf caller again and nothing happened. I wrapped my jacket tighter around me and shivered.

"Here, Jennie. Have some of this." Father poured a steaming cup of cocoa into the thermos cap and handed it to me. "Stay here and warm up," he ordered. "I'm going to take a look over that next ridge."

I sipped the hot drink gratefully as he left the lean-to and strode off. The sun peeped over the hill opposite me and I gazed in wonder at its glory. Palo verdes and clumps of cactus became living things instead of mere shadows.

"O Jesus," I breathed, "thank You for letting us enjoy all Your creation. And thanks for loving and caring for us as You do." I loved the Lord so much and never ceased to be amazed at His goodness. The fun things our family did—such as this—and our Sunday worship at church made my life seem peaceful and complete.

Warmer, I munched a handful of raisins and peanuts, leaning forward to peer between the cracks. Father had disappeared over the top of the ridge and everything was quiet.

Suddenly, something in the distance caught my attention. I stared hard into the early morning light at what looked like a dark shadow on the trail above me. I was

Wolves on the Trail

sure I had seen something move!

Silently, a second gray shape joined the first, then another and another. I held my breath as they moved closer and closer. From my position, about 100 feet away, I could see that the animals were about the size of German shepherd dogs, only much thinner. An unexpected tremor ran through me as I realized that they were *wolves!*

At first I was more thrilled than scared. The animals moved quietly closer, stopping to sniff the air and the trail every few feet. I placed my cup on the ground next to me and sat perfectly still, afraid to startle the furry forms with the bright, yellowish eyes.

As the wolves approached, I could see their ribs standing out and the hungry look on their faces. *Where is Father?* I wondered nervously. *Will the animals stop to check out the lean-to or will they pass quietly on down the trail?*

The wolves crept to within ten feet of me. I wanted to scream for help then, but my throat seemed to have frozen shut. I wondered if the shelter would be strong enough to protect me if they should decide to attack. It was unlikely, I knew, but those wolves sure looked lean and hungry!

"Jesus," I prayed silently, "I'm scared. Please protect me and keep Father safe too. Thanks."

Suddenly Father's voice came from the top of a nearby ridge. "Run to the jeep, Jennie!" he yelled. "I'll cover you."

At his cry, the animals ran back up the trail 100 feet or so. I jumped up only to find that my left leg was numb and wouldn't hold me. The cramped position I'd been sitting in had put it to sleep. "I can't, Father," I called back.

He raised his rifle, pointed it toward the sky, then pulled the trigger several times. At the loud cracks, the wolves turned and ran with their tails between their legs.

"Thanks, Jesus," I whispered in relief before limping out of the lean-to to meet Father who was running toward me.

He hugged me tightly. "I sure didn't intend for you to watch wolves that close up," he apologized.

"That's all right, Father," I said smiling. "Jesus kept me safe while you were gone and helped me not to be too scared."

"We'll stick together from now on," Father said as we climbed the hill. "And we'll do our wolf-calling from inside the jeep. OK?"

"Sounds good to me," I agreed with a grin.

Patrick's Butterfly

A TRUE STORY
by Margaret Lacey

Patrick, his parents, sister Mary, and brother James were visiting Grandmother and Grandfather on their farm. One morning after it had rained, Patrick ran out into the front yard. On the ground he found a large butterfly that could not fly. Her wings were torn at the edges.

Carefully, because he knew it hurt a butterfly to pick it up by its wings, Patrick put his hand down beside the butterfly and let her climb onto his finger. When she started to walk on his hand, her tickly feet made Patrick giggle. The butterfly's wings were black and blue and yellow. On the bottom of each was a bright orange spot with a black dot in the middle.

"Look at my butterfly," Patrick said to his grandmother, who was sitting in the porch swing, shelling peas. "Isn't she beautiful? See, she has orange eyes on her wings. Can I keep her for a pet?"

"I doubt if she'll live long, Patrick. She can't fly. But bring her in the house," Grandmother said.

Patrick watched the butterfly for a while. Grandmother looked in a book and found a picture just like it. She showed it to him. "See—she's called a swallowtail."

"Does the book say anything about what swallowtails eat?" Patrick asked.

"No, it just has pictures," Grandmother answered. "But maybe we could try some of the honey and water I've made for the hummingbirds." She brought some to Patrick in a bottle cap. "Put a drop on your finger," she said.

For a while nothing happened. Then Patrick yelled, "Grandmother, she's unrolling her NOSE! And she's using it to drink!"

"She certainly is," Grandmother said, looking over his shoulder.

Patrick fed the butterfly until she wouldn't eat any more. Grandmother brought a box, and they put the butterfly in it with some honey and water. She stayed there all day, waving her wings.

103

When Patrick was not playing in the yard or helping with chores, he watched his butterfly. Sometimes he would take her out and let her walk up his arm because he liked the tickly feel of her feet. She unrolled her nose and ate lots of honey and water from his finger.

Patrick let James and Mary hold the butterfly and feed her too. They played with the butterfly until it was time for all of them to go to bed.

When Patrick came downstairs the next morning the box was empty. "Where is she?" Patrick cried. "Who took my butterfly?" He and the family looked everywhere in the house for the missing butterfly.

Finally Grandfather called out, "I see her. She's in this room. Can you find her?"

Patrick looked and looked. Then all at once he saw a big bright flower on one of the plants in the window. But it wasn't a flower. It was his butterfly.

"But I thought you said she couldn't fly anymore, Grandmother," the boy said excitedly.

"All that rest and food you gave her made her stronger, Patrick," Grandmother answered.

The butterfly sat on his finger, but this time she did not stay there. When she was through eating, she flew toward the window again. Sometimes she would come over to land on Patrick's shoulder and eat some more. Once she even sat on his head for a while, but she always went back to the window. When he went to bed that night, Patrick had to put a piece of screen on top of the box to keep the butterfly from getting lost again.

The butterfly did not like staying in the box anymore. Patrick found her beating her wings against the screen when he got up. All morning the butterfly sat in the sunniest windows or beat her wings against the glass.

Mom was watching the butterfly too. Finally, she put her arm around Patrick's shoulder and said, "I think you have helped her become so strong that she wants to go and live outdoors again."

"Oh, no," Patrick said quickly. "I want to take her home with me and keep her a long time. She's my pet now and needs me to give her food."

Mom didn't say anything else, but Patrick noticed that the butterfly spent more and more time beating her wings against the windows. He began to be afraid she would hurt herself. He watched her and thought for a long time. Then he went over to where his dad was reading.

After a while Dad said, "What is it, Patrick?"

"I know my butterfly wants to be free, but I want to keep her so much," Patrick said with a sob.

"I know," Dad said.

"Daddy, I'm afraid she might starve because she wouldn't have me to feed her honey and water," Patrick said.

"Well," answered Dad, "I think her long nose will help her eat nectar from the flowers like the bees do."

Patrick thought some more. Then he went over to the window and let the butterfly crawl onto his finger. "Come on, Dad," he said.

Patrick and his father went out onto the porch. Patrick kept one hand cupped over the other. When he took it away, the butterfly sat for a few moments waving its wings. Then she flew high up into the air.

"Where is she? I can't see her anymore," Patrick shouted.

"There she is, over the cornfield," Dad answered. "Look how well she flies."

They stood on the edge of the porch and watched the butterfly. Beating her wings strongly, she flew away over the corn rows until she became a tiny speck and disappeared.

Patrick rubbed his eyes and leaned against his dad. "I'm glad she can fly away, but I still feel sad," he whispered.

Dad gave him a hug. Then he and Patrick sat on the porch swing for a while and looked at the sunny place in the cornfield where the butterfly had gone.

Betsy Doesn't Know It's Stealing

A FICTION STORY
by Kermit Shelby

Betsy, the white German shepherd pup, had done it again. Matt Wiggins stood still, viewing with delight, then guilt, the beautiful bone-handled jackknife lying on the doormat.

The pup watched him. Betsy was waiting for praise or the bacon scrap Matt always gave her when she did a new trick.

But where did she find the knife? Matt wondered. He stooped over and ran his finger carefully along its razor-sharp blade. It was silky smooth. The knife felt good in his hand when he tried it for size.

"I'd sure like to try it out on my carving, Betsy," he told his pup.

"Hey, Mom. Come see what Betsy brought us this time," Matt called.

His mother came to the doorway with a dish towel in her hands. Matt showed her the knife. "Isn't it great? Just what I needed for carving my mountain man.

"Looks like you read my mind, Betsy. Good dog." Matt patted her on the head. "Mom, have we got any more bacon scraps for Betsy?"

"Bacon scraps cost money, Matt. You know we can't afford to give bacon scraps to your dog," his mother said. "I'm not going to reward her. Neither that old shoe or the worn-out glove she brought home was worth anything. But this knife is valuable. You must try to find the owner."

"But, Mom, the man at the gas station sold my carved figure of a Grandma-chopping-wood for a dollar and gave me orders for more. My old knife won't cut anything and the handle is broken."

Matt felt as if something wonderful were about to be snatched from him. "Besides, Betsy doesn't know it's stealing."

"There—you defined it yourself. *Stealing,*" Mrs. Wiggins said. "Betsy doesn't know the difference. But we do and so does Jesus."

"OK, Mom, I'll go see if I can find the owner." Secretly, Matt wondered if it really would matter to the Lord if he didn't try too hard.

"It could belong to Mr. Bradley or his helper at the gas station," Mrs. Wiggins said. "Better try the people who own Silver Falls Cave too. They've been doing a lot of building, adding on new souvenir shops."

Matt and Betsy set off down the road. They stopped first at the gas station. Joe Bradley admired the jackknife, but he admitted it wasn't his. "Why don't you finish your carvings first, Matt? Then you can find the owner."

"Mom said it's the same as stealing."

"How can a pup steal?" Joe asked. "She doesn't know what she's doing. Do you, Betsy?"

"But *we* do. And so does God," Matt said. He felt a little less disappointed as he walked the half mile to Silver Falls Cave.

Matt seldom went near the expensive tourist shops. His mother was a widow who worked for Mrs. Yancey, cleaning motel rooms. Matt had no money to spend—not even for the coming Christmas.

He stopped, enchanted, looking at a shop window display of the Christ Child lying in a wooden manger. It was beautifully hand-carved from cedar.

Matt and Betsy walked into the shop. Cedar shavings lay everywhere. Matt could smell the rich wood smells before he reached the man working with a chisel and electric drill on a huge picture. The picture and the frame were carved from the same piece of wood. The picture wasn't finished yet, but underneath were the hand-carved letters, "The Lord's Supper."

"Say, that's really something," Matt said, awed.

The carver turned. His eyes were the color of sunlight on water. He sounded kindly, but preoccupied. "Like this mural, Son? Help yourself. We have quite a collection." He motioned toward the aisle lined with wooden Indians, elephants, bookends, and a three-ring circus. Every item was hand-carved from wood.

Matt was speechless.

"My name's David Topps," the carver said. "I think I've seen your pup around here before." He paused and looked at his work, shaking his head. "I'm not doing so good today. Lost my favorite carving knife. One moment it was over there on a block of wood. The next moment it was gone. A tourist must have taken it."

Matt reached into his pocket and pulled out the knife. "Is this it?" he asked.

The carver's eyes lighted with surprise. "That's my knife, all right."

Matt said, embarrassed, "Betsy, the pup—. You see, at home I reward her with bacon scraps when she does tricks. She brings stuff home. She thinks they're presents. I've still got to train her a lot," Matt said. Then he remembered, "Oh, yes—is this glove yours too?"

"Never laid eyes on the glove, but—" Dave Topps stopped. He picked up the tiny carved figure that fell out of Matt's pocket when he pulled out the glove. "Say, that's clever," he said, admiring the half-finished, barefooted figure. "Did you make this?"

Matt nodded. "But I broke my knife, so it isn't finished."

"I could sell these. Come here a minute," Mr. Topps said. He led the way to a workbench and pulled out a drawer. Matt had never seen so many knives. "The one you brought back was my favorite," the man explained. "But I want you to know I'm grateful. Take your pick."

Matt knew he shouldn't take the best one. He chose a medium-looking knife with a sharp blade of blue steel. "This will do fine. Thank you."

"If you have time after school or on Saturdays, I could use an honest boy like you around the shop. Bring me some more hand-carved mountain men and I'll sell them for you. Try this piece of cedar to start with. Don't worry about knives. We've got quite a supply."

Matt's eyes got all swimmy. "C-could you show me how to carve the Christ Child in the manger?" he asked.

"I'll teach you all I know, Son."

"Please call me Matt."

The man smiled. "OK, Matt."

"Thanks, Mr. Topps. I'll be back." Matt whistled to Betsy and they started home. Matt stroked the new knife in his pocket. It felt wonderful. He stopped and patted Betsy. "First mountain man we sell, Betsy, it's bacon scraps for you," Matt promised.

Betsy wagged her tail and took off after a rabbit.

The World's Tallest Animal

by Gloria A. Truitt

As the world's tallest animal
(I measure eighteen feet,)
I reach the tippy-tops of trees
To get the leaves I eat.
Because I have no vocal cords,
The best that I can do,
Whenever I must make a sound
Is softly whisper, "Moo."
If your neck was as long as mine,
I'm sure that folks would laugh,
For no one is as tall as me,
The African giraffe!

Taller Than the Treetops

A NATURE STORY
by Elaine Watson

How would you like to be taller than a tree, run faster than a horse, and be able to kill a lion with one swift blow from your foot? Well, you could if you were a giraffe, the tallest animal in the world.

When you hear the name *giraffe,* what do you think of first? Most people think of a tall, orange animal with brown spots and a long neck.

A male giraffe sometimes reaches a height of 18 feet and weighs over two tons (4,000 pounds). That means he is also one of the world's four largest animals, along with the elephant, hippopotamus, and rhinoceros.

A giraffe's neck may be over six feet long! But, amazingly, a giraffe and a mouse have the same number of bones in their necks. Both have seven. Of course, the giraffe's are much larger!

Because of his height and long neck, the giraffe must go through quite a bit to get a drink from a stream or a lake. He either has to bend his legs or spread them far apart.

He never kneels to drink because he wouldn't be able to see danger nearby from that position. And he usually sleeps standing up.

Scientists believe that giraffes once ranged over Europe and Asia. But the ancient Egyptians were the first to record anything about them. Drawings and paintings of giraffes have been found in Egyptian tombs.

In 46 B.C. Julius Caesar introduced the giraffe to Rome by parading it down the streets of the city. Many people knew about the huge, long-necked, gentle animal. But most people would not believe the giraffe existed until they saw it themselves.

The Chinese thought highly of the giraffe. The emperor often received giraffes as gifts. For almost 10 years, the Chinese considered this curious animal an emblem of perfect virtue, perfect government, and perfect harmony in the empire and universe.

Starting around 1870, giraffes were first used in circuses and shown in zoos. In 1874, a female giraffe and five males were brought to the U.S. by the Zoological Society of Philadelphia.

Today, the giraffe's home is Africa. He likes the dry, open bush country where there are plenty of acacia (uh-KAY-shah) trees. The leaves of these trees are his favorite food. He can eat from the treetops and at the same time watch for other animals.

He has excellent eyesight and can easily spot danger such as a hunter or hungry lion. The giraffe protects himself by hiding among trees where his orange coat and brown spots blend with the brush.

If a lion attacks him, he can kill it with one well-aimed kick. A mother giraffe, when attacked, will place her baby between her front legs while she fights.

A very intelligent and sociable animal, the giraffe has a life span of about twenty-eight years. He usually travels in a herd of up to twenty giraffes. A male giraffe, called a bull, leads the herd. The females, called cows, watch for danger. A newborn giraffe weighs from 110 to 250 pounds and is usually from five to six feet tall. Within an hour after birth, he can walk around.

The giraffe is a graceful animal and moves with rhythm. He can walk, trot, run, and gallop—sometimes galloping faster than a horse. He has been known to reach a speed of over thirty miles an hour! But he is a poor wader and can't swim at all.

Giraffes will never purposely bother anyone, but their height has been known to get them into trouble. One became tangled in telegraph lines once and put 600 miles of wire out of order.

The giraffe is quiet. He rarely uses his voice because he doesn't have to. But when captured, he will grunt or bleat. Males will grunt or cough and females have been known to make a snoring sound.

When God made the giraffe, He made a unique and amazing animal.

The next time you go to the zoo, visit this orange spotted giant. But don't wear a hat trimmed with flowers or leaves. He eats by sight, not by smell, and he might enjoy your hat for dessert.

Bingo's Accident!

A TRUE STORY
by Cindy Kightlinger

It was a cool October evening. Jenna Kightlinger and her family had been out visiting all day. When they pulled into their driveway ten-year-old Jenna wondered why her collie, Bingo, didn't run out barking as usual. Then she saw a note taped to the garage door. "Look, Dad!" she cried.

He shone the car headlights on the note, then got out and read it.

"What is it, Dad?" Jenna asked as she jumped out of the car.

He handed the note to Jenna's mother and Jenna read it with her. It said that their neighbor had hit Bingo with his car when Bingo ran out in front of him. Worse yet, Bingo would not let the man carry him to his car, so the dog was lying by the fence in the front yard.

Mom and Jenna hurried into the house. Jenna found a flashlight and took it to her father. He raced to the fence, but Bingo wasn't there. Frantically, Dad searched the yard. Then Mom turned on the porch light and there was Bingo, crumpled up on the porch.

"Dad!" Jenna screamed. "Look at his face!" She reached out to stroke her pet's puffy head, but Dad pushed her hand away.

"He's in pain, Honey. He may bite you."

"Is he going to die?" Jenna asked.

"I don't know. I have to get him to the vet. Get me something to muzzle him."

Jenna brought out a clean rag and Dad gently tied it around Bingo's long nose. The dog didn't growl or move.

As soon as Dad lifted Bingo, Jenna saw that something was wrong with the dog's front leg. "It's just hanging!" Jenna gasped.

Carefully, Dad placed Bingo in the car. "I'll call when I know something," he yelled as he jumped in and sped off.

"Why did God let Bingo get hit?" Jenna cried. "God is supposed to protect us. I hate Him! Bingo is going to die now!"

"Jenna," Mom said quietly, "God did watch out for Bingo. That car could have killed him. Let's pray and believe that God will heal Bingo."

"I don't want to pray. God let my dog get hurt," Jenna said.

Mom tried to put her arms around Jenna, but Jenna pulled away and ran to her room. She was there when the phone rang. She heard Mother say something about "amputation" and "going to sleep." Then Mom shouted, "I don't care what it costs. Fix that dog!"

Jenna ran to her mother. "Is Bingo all right? Is he going to live?"

"The vet says that the bones in his front leg and shoulder were crushed. He needs an operation."

117

"Mom," Jenna asked, "what is *amputation?*"

Mom's face got red and she put her arms around Jenna. "The vet may not be able to save Bingo's leg," she explained.

Suddenly, Jenna wasn't angry anymore. She was too scared. This reminded her of the time when Grandma was real sick and Mom had said all they could do was pray and have faith that God would heal her.

Bingo stayed at the animal hospital for two weeks. Jenna was allowed to visit him. When she crawled into his large cage, he opened his eyes a slit, whimpered, and went back to sleep.

Jenna looked at the cast on his leg and stroked his head. "It's OK, Bingo," she whispered. "I prayed and believe God will heal you." Bingo opened his eyes again and pressed his nose against her.

When they brought Bingo home, Mom had Jenna fix up a bed in the basement. Jenna put together old blankets, even an old pillow for Bingo's sore leg. Fluffing the blankets around him, she vowed to take care of her pet and thanked God for bringing him home again.

Bingo had to visit the vet each week and take pills. Otherwise, all he could do most of the winter was lie still, eat, and sleep.

In the weeks that followed Jenna grew impatient. "Mom, why isn't God healing Bingo?" she asked.

"He is," Mom answered. "But we must be patient."

"God's had all winter and Bingo still can't get around much. How long will God take?"

When spring came, Dad carried Bingo outside for fresh air on sunny days. Jenna often sat by her dog, stroking him, and wondering how long it would be till he could run beside her or trek through the woods with her again.

Gradually, Bingo grew stronger. He'd stumble to the end of the drive, sit and rest, then stumble back to the garage. After walking any distance, he needed hours of rest.

One day Jenna said, "Mom, it's been almost a year and Bingo still isn't himself. See how he limps!"

"Jenna, we aren't the way we used to be either. Remember how we took Bingo for granted—how we'd tell him he was a pest when we wanted to be left alone? But now we love him for himself, not for what he can do."

"And I guess I've learned that sometimes I have to wait for something really special, like God healing Bingo," Jenna said thoughtfully.

"Yes, we've learned a lot about trusting the Lord when things look hopeless—and about waiting," Mother added. "I think God has been 'healing' us too, don't you?"

" I HATE SLUMBER PARTIES. "

Shark Bay

A FICTION STORY
by Karen M. Leet

Marc froze, his knuckles white as he gripped the edge of the raft and peered down into the clear water of the bay. He could not believe what he was seeing.

But his eyes insisted. The dark, sleek shape slid past the swimmers' raft again. Instinctively, Marc scooted away from the edge. Staring into the water, he saw the shark glide in great, swooping circles close to the sandy bottom of the swimming area.

Then it was gone. Marc pulled his legs up under his body and tried to concentrate. The wooden raft beneath him had felt firm only moments ago. Now the planks looked thin and water-rotted.

Marc wondered how big the shark actually was. Probably not as big as it seemed. Water distorts sizes. He tried to convince himself that the shark wasn't a great danger.

It probably wouldn't attack the wooden raft either. Why should it? Maybe it wasn't even interested in him. Maybe it didn't even know he was there.

The shark appeared again. Was it closer to the surface now? It turned abruptly and swam directly under the flimsy raft. Marc clenched his teeth until his jaws ached. Gooseflesh prickled his cold, wet skin.

He wanted to yell for help and keep yelling till someone appeared. Trembling slightly from cold, Marc looked toward the beach again. But he knew no one was there.

Marc had known better than to swim alone—especially out to the raft. He had lied to his mom, telling her he had been invited to the bay to swim with John Whitefeather. It hadn't exactly been a lie. John *had* invited him. But Marc hadn't wanted to be friends with John anymore. John was an Indian. He lived on the reservation and the other guys made fun of him.

Anyway, Marc sneaked down to the reservation bay alone, long before John or any of the other Indians arrived. He knew the Indian boy would be working in the tribal gardens for most of the afternoon.

Marc shuddered. Seeing the stretch of empty beach made him feel so alone. He wrapped his arms tight around his chest. He only had to wait until the Indian boys finished their chores. They'd be sure to come swimming afterward.

Marc would be safe then. One of the boys would run for help. Someone would drag out one of the old rowboats propped along the far end of the beach. And he'd be rescued.

Where was that shark? The bay water looked calm and peaceful now. Marc wished he could believe the shark was gone. He wished he could plunge back into the clear water, swim smoothly to shore, dry off with his tattered towel, and bike home.

Suddenly, something bumped the raft. The wooden

planks vibrated from the impact. Marc almost jumped to his feet, but before he could move he saw the shark. It glided out from under the platform, rose almost to the surface, banked gently, and drifted away.

Marc found himself praying frantically for help. He couldn't remember when he'd last prayed. But he was praying now, and telling God he was sorry for ignoring Him for such a long time. Marc felt ashamed of all the times he'd pretended to be sick so he wouldn't have to go to Sunday School. He felt embarrassed that he'd tried to impress his friends at school by showing off and making fun of the boys who went to Sunday School.

Something bumped the raft again. Marc slipped sideways, off-balance. The water was close to him. The platform seemed smaller.

Without realizing that he still remembered it, Marc began murmuring the Lord's Prayer. Over and over he repeated the words. He began to feel calmer. He could still see the shark lazily swinging through the water, sometimes very close to the raft.

The shark bumped the wooden planks three more times while Marc waited for help. He didn't feel as panicky now. In a way, he felt sort of safe. He knew God was taking care of him.

When he saw a boy striding through the scrub grass toward the white, sandy beach, Marc recognized John and waved his arms over his head. Then he cupped his hands and shouted across the water, hoping John would understand. "Shark!"

John must have gotten the message. He stopped, waved, then sprinted across the beach to the rowboats. He dragged one of the sturdy, wooden boats to the edge of the water and pushed it in. Hopping in, he rowed swiftly to the raft.

Once the shark rose to the surface, and both boys saw the ominous black fin cut through the water near the boat.

What if the boat capsized? What if John lost the oars? What if the shark rammed it? Marc's head was full of doubts. Quietly, he began praying again and he grew calmer.

The boat bumped against the platform and Marc eased carefully into it. In less than five minutes, both boys were safe on the beach.

Marc rubbed himself with his towel and pulled on his shirt.

"Listen, John," he said, unable to meet the Indian boy's eyes. "I'm sorry I've been hanging around with the guys who make fun of you and the others from the reservation. I was wrong. You and I have been friends for a long time. I hope we can still be friends."

Marc finally looked at his Indian friend. John nodded and smiled. Then he grabbed one side of the boat and Marc grabbed the other side and both boys dragged it back to the far end of the beach.

John glanced back at the bay. "We'd better tell the council about the shark. Some of the men will probably come back and chase him out and mend the net at the bay entrance." John looked at Marc then. "Want to help?"

"Sure," Marc agreed, grinning at his friend. "But I'll have to check with my parents first."

"OK," John said, nodding.

Together the boys jogged to their bikes, cheerfully arguing over which one had been more afraid of the shark, how big it really was, and whether it could have eaten the rowboat or turned the raft over.

THE ANIMAL TAILS SERIES

These heartwarming stories, poems, and cartoons will help you discover God's care for all His creatures. Be sure to read all the books in the Animal Tails series:

The Hairy Brown Angel and Other Animal Tails

The Peanut Butter Hamster and Other Animal Tails

Skunk for Rent and Other Animal Tails

The Incompetent Cat and Other Animal Tails

The Duck Who Had Goosebumps and Other Animal Tails

The Pint-Sized Piglet and Other Animal Tails

The Hopeless Hen and Other Animal Tails

THE EXITORN ADVENTURES

Visit the make-believe kingdom of Exitorn where you'll meet 12-year-old Brill and his daredevil friend, Segra. Their fast-paced fantasy stories will keep you turning the pages to see what will happen next.

Brill and the Dragators

Brill longs for his humble farm home when he is brought to the palace as a companion to the crown prince. The emperor and his son live only for pleasure and Brill remembers how different they are from his grandfather who lives for God. Will Brill and Segra be able to help the former king escape from prison? (6-1344)

Segra and Stargull

Segra and Brill journey through Exitorn, across stormy seas, and into a neighboring country seeking Segra's parents. Their adventures call for courage and faith as time and again Segra risks her life and Brill's to help someone in need. (6-1345)

Segra in Diamond Castle

Segra is kidnapped and held prisoner by Umber in Diamond Castle. When her escape attempts fail, she comes up with a plan to outsmart Umber and end his war with Exitorn (6-1449).

Winner Books are produced by Victor Books and are designed to entertain and instruct young readers in Christian principles.

Other Winner Books you will enjoy:

Dear Reader:
We would like to know your thoughts about the book you've just read. Your ideas will help us as we seek to publish books that will interest you.

Send your responses to:

Winner Books
1825 College Avenue
Wheaton, IL 60187

What made you decide to read The Hopeless Hen?

☐ I bought it for myself.

☐ My parents bought it for me.

☐ It was a gift.

☐ It was part of a school assignment.

☐ It was loaned to me by a friend.

What did you like most about this book? (You can check more than one answer.)

☐ Characters

☐ Story

☐ Mystery

☐ Animals

☐ Romance

☐ Adventure

☐ Humor

☐ Inside art sketches

☐ Glossary

☐ Other: _____

From the following list, please check the subjects you would like to read about in the future. (You can check more than one answer.)

☐ Sports

☐ Make-believe

☐ Science fiction

☐ Animals

☐ Real people

☐ History

☐ Scary stories

☐ Mysteries

☐ Comics

☐ Devotional books

☐ Other: _____

Would you be interested in reading other Winner books? (Check only one answer.)
- ☐ Very interested
- ☐ A little bit interested
- ☐ Not at all interested

How old are you?
- ☐ Under 8
- ☐ 8
- ☐ 9
- ☐ 10
- ☐ 11
- ☐ 12
- ☐ Over 12

Would you be interested in a Winner book club? If so, please fill in your name and address below:

Name: _____

_____

ADDRESS: _____

_____